A
Harlequin
Romance

OTHER
Harlequin Romances
by AMANDA DOYLE

1085—A CHANGE FOR CLANCY
1116—PLAY THE TUNE SOFTLY
1190—THE SHADOW AND THE SUN
1239—THIS WISH I HAVE
1308—A MIST IN GLEN TORRAN
1351—THE GIRL FOR GILLGONG
1448—THE YEAR AT YATTABILLA
1486—THE POST AT GUNDOOEE
1527—DILEMMA AT DULLOORA
1562—KOOKABURRA DAWN

ESCAPE TO KOOLONGA

by

AMANDA DOYLE

HARLEQUIN BOOKS   TORONTO
WINNIPEG

Original hard cover edition published in 1972
by Mills & Boon Limited, 17 - 19 Foley Street
London W1A 1DR, England

© Amanda Doyle 1972

Harlequin edition published October, 1972

SBN 373-01630-1

Printed in Canada

CHAPTER ONE

PLAIN JANE.

She wasn't Jane at all, really, she was Emmie. Or, more properly, Emily. Emily Montfort.

But she thought of herself as a Jane, and a plain one at that.

Emmie supposed it was bound to happen, when you turned out to be the only ordinary duckling in a clutch of quite brilliant offspring. Not only had the other members of the Montfort family been endowed with brains and drive and thrusting personalities and a business acumen which led them all quite painlessly along the paths of success in their chosen field, but they had also been favoured quite bountifully by Nature herself with the famous Montfort 'good looks'--things like that wonderful Montfort hair, for example, either a deep and glowing auburn or an abundant raven black; the marvellous Montfort bone-structure, which made for long, interesting faces in the males, and moulded, sculptured, mysterious ones in the females of the line; the well-spaced Montfort eyes, that were nearly all a bold, snapping brown regardless of auburn or raven heads; and the Montfort smiles which were all perfect, charming and delightful because of the evenness and whiteness of the strong, sound Montfort teeth. As for the Montfort physique, it had all the qualities that spell perfection too—good proportions, adequate stature (the women, by and large, might almost be described as tall for their sex, but more often than not you'd have called them 'willowy', because that was what they were), and the men were muscular and athletic, the girls enviably vital and vivacious.

Only Emmie was the exception. The plain Jane.

They used to call her that sometimes, when they were all

little, in those moments of childish frustration when brothers and sisters want to inflict hurt intentionally. Emmie had resisted, had risen to the taunts in quick, uncontrollable bouts of rage.

Now they didn't say it any more. Being adults, they merely implied it, probably quite *un*intentionally, and Emmie, being also adult, accepted the implications philosophically, with an equanimity which in childhood she had not possessed.

Her mirror told her the truth, that those implications were quite justifiable. That straight brown hair, even supposing it was fine and silky and always shining with cleanliness, had nothing of the fiery splendour of her sister Melissa's, nor the blue-black sleekness of Sharon's gleaming mane. Her face was small and inclined to pallor, an uninteresting oval, devoid of those prominent bones and intriguing hollows that made Lissa's and Sharon's almost classic Montfort. Her eyes were well-spaced, certainly, but with a width and innocence that could not compare with the challenge and assurance of the others'. And although they were appealing eyes, hers, fringed with a sweep of thickly dark, curling lashes—her best feature, perhaps—they were also of a common hazel-grey, neither one thing nor the other. When she wore greys and blues and greens they were grey, and when she wore reds and browns and yellows they were hazel. Chameleon eyes, as if Nature hadn't quite been able to make up her mind what to do about them. Emmie's chin was small and oval to match her face, and her mouth was wide, if anything too generous, and when she smiled her teeth were pearly-crooked, which meant that her smile wasn't the enviably flashing, white, strong Montfort smile either. Not like Sharon's or Lissa's, or Mark's or Robert's. The boys—well, they were *men* now, actually—were a handsome pair, aristocratic, confident, quite marvellously good-looking in the typical Montfort manner. They were big men, too. Tall, athletic, just as Sharon and Lissa were *willowy*.

Emmie herself wasn't willowy.

6

Not dumpy, actually, either. Just *diminutive*. You wouldn't look at her twice in a crowd, because she'd be lost to view amongst all those other heads.

Plain? Well—rather, unremarkable.

That was it, quite unremarkable.

And so far, her achievements in life had been singularly unremarkable, too, compared with those of the rest of the family. After all, there was Mark, the eldest, a flourishing barrister; Robert with his new consulting-rooms, already recognised as one of Sydney's up-and-coming young paediatricians; Melissa, who had made what might be described as a 'good marriage', and who had so cunningly managed to place her two beautiful children in the care of the most reliable and dependable of domestic staff while she travelled extensively with her diplomat husband; and the youngest, Sharon, not yet at the peak of her career as a promising model.

Emmie came between the two other sisters, and people seeing them all together never failed to be amazed at that fact.

Sometimes they voiced the amazement in guileless remarks, like 'Goodness, are they really your sisters? Such glamorous girls, aren't they!', or, peering at her, 'Yes, that's right, there is a slight family resemblance, of course there is—I can see, now that I *look*!'

Even worse, the few things Emmie had, or even hadn't achieved, had been done, or not done, she suspected, because of her connection with the other members of the Montfort family, and not because of what she was herself.

'Is Mark Montfort *really* your brother? Well, I suppose we could arrange an interview.'

'I'm sorry, very sorry, that you've become redundant, Miss Montfort. We hate to disappoint a sister of Robert's.'

'Most regrettable, but I feel perhaps that your talents lie in other directions, my dear. We're all individuals, I mean, aren't we, and even sisters can differ.'

It wasn't just the people outside the family who thought

7

like that, either.

Inside it, too, she was apt simply to be overlooked in the rush. When those two handsome brothers had been younger, it was Lissa and Sharon who gained the lion's share of their attention, and undoubtedly they merited that attention, too. Emmie was prepared to admit it with typical humility. She became accustomed to hearing them making plans together, and on the rare occasions when she found herself included, to suffer the inevitable surprised comments—'What? Another sister of Mark's and Robbie's? We know Sharon and Lissa, of course, but you are a bit of a shock, I must say. Where on earth have they been hiding you?'

Even when she got accustomed to all these observations, even when she had learned to accept them, yet Emmie still found that they depressed her.

More and more she avoided the sort of situations in which they were likely to occur, more and more she found herself staying away from the sort of functions where they were likely to happen.

It was natural, she supposed, that when her parents died, the others should look to her to stay at home and take care of them all—to be there when Mark came back, irritable after a trying session at the law-courts; when Robert returned, weary and preoccupied after a harrowing day at the Children's Hospital; when Sharon appeared, languid and cross and lovely, after too many late nights and a gruelling modelling assignment; or when Lissa's 'treasure' was having her 'days off', and the children had to be left in someone else's care.

Yes, Emmie was there, always there. And, at twenty-six, it looked as if she always would be. Her only talent was the simple art of being in the right place, at the right time, when the family happened to have need of her.

They all took it for granted now, even Emmie herself.

For a while, she had taken a part-time job as a librarian, and had thoroughly enjoyed it, but the hours hadn't fitted in with the rest of the family's requirements.

Lissa complained that her children were being neglected while she was away. Surely it wasn't asking too much——?

Mark complained that his dinner wasn't ready, and that she must know by now what a brief lunch interval he sometimes had—he'd been too busy today, interviewing a witness, to have more than a sandwich and a coffee.

Robert's laundry wasn't done—and he had to have those starched white coats looking fresh and dazzling, didn't he?

And Sharon—well, Sharon's criticisms of her elder sister's inconvenient absence at the library for a few irregular hours each day were almost too numerous to begin to be catalogued!

Emmie sometimes thought to herself that they had become so used to having her at their beck and call that they had ceased to think about her at all, or even to remember that she was there.

Perhaps that was why they were all gathered in the living-room just now, looking mildly surprised that someone else had remembered her, and even more surprised that the someone happened to be the late Miss Millicent.

Miss Millicent had been their governess for years, right down the family, from the oldest Montfort child to the youngest Montfort child, all the time they were growing up.

Emmie could remember her very well indeed. Millie, they had called her, for short. She had been a comfortable and comforting figure, always there, just as Emmie herself was 'always there' right now. She had had a flat, uninteresting face enlivened by a pair of beady bright eyes that spotted every bit of mischief almost before it had been begun, and her pepper-and-salty brown hair had been done up in two coils on either side of her head.

Miss Millicent did not seem to have any relatives of her own. She had always laughed and told them that *they* were her family, whenever Emmie had asked her. After she had left them—once Sharon had outgrown the need for a governess—the family had kept up a spasmodic correspondence with her, and then, as they became older, even that tenuous contact had gradually lapsed. Only Emmie had remembered Miss Millicent, and then it was a once-yearly occasion, at Christmas time, when they faithfully exchanged letters telling each other of the whole year's doings in between these seasonal festivities. Emmie did not have a great deal to report about herself, but she was able to tell Miss Millicent all about Mark's continuing success as a barrister, and Robert's appointment at the hospital, and Lissa's lovely children, and Sharon's popularity with the fashion people. Like Emmie, Miss Millicent didn't have a great deal to report, either. For a time she had taken care of an elderly father, and when her parent died she had got a job as a companion to an irritable old woman who apparently almost drove Millie to distraction with her demanding ways. Last Christmas there had been no word from Miss Millicent, although Emmie had faithfully reported in a six-page document upon the varying progress of each member of the Montfort family, and had sent the letter to the governess's last address. When no reply was forthcoming, she had been forced to conclude that either Miss Millicent had indeed been driven to final distraction of the permanent, incurable variety, or that she had lost the urge to exchange gossip with a family which, after all these years, must undoubtedly have become too remote to be interesting any longer.

As it turned out, Emmie could not have been more wrong in assuming that she had been forgotten. Instead, she had been remembered, and in a very concrete and practical manner.

'A *general* store!' Sharon was exclaiming at this very moment—draped over one end of the couch in a consciously lovely pose, with that curtain of raven's-wing hair falling about her shoulders, and derision causing her expressive brown Montfort eyes to glint mockingly. 'What a terribly odd thing to be left, for sure! And what was Millie thinking of, leaving it to *you*, anyway, Emm? I mean, I was her "baby", wasn't I? She always *said* so.' Sharon sounded injured.

'I suppose I've kept in touch with her more than the rest of you. I mean, you are all so busy, and I've had more time to write, haven't I?' Emmie hastened to point out. She was still quite overcome with surprise herself, actually. 'And in a way I can just imagine Millie running a little shop, can't you, especially in the country. She always wanted to go back to the country, you know, when she retired. What a shame that she appears to have had so little joy out of her move, poor old thing. Just eighteen months, and then to—to die, so very suddenly.'

'She wouldn't have suffered, Emmie.' Robert was instantly aware of his sister's genuine distress. 'She would have had little or no foreknowledge at all, with a thing like that. Dear old Millie, she wasn't a bad old stick.'

'But—a *shop*!' Sharon giggled. 'What on earth would Emmie do with a *shop*? And, as I said, I can't for the life of me see why it should be Emm, in particular. Why not have left it to *all* of us, and then we could sell the asset—if it is one, which is doubtful!—and divide the proceeds?'

'I expect she recognised the fact that Emmie might—well —that Emmie might be glad enough of the proceeds herself, don't you think?' That was Melissa, reproving Sharon on Emmie's behalf. Emmie knew quite well that what Melissa really meant was that Emmie had no marriage prospects, none at all, although she didn't actually say that in so many words. 'In any case,' continued Lissa calmly, 'Emmie *can* sell it, can't she? It's the obvious thing to do. You could travel a little, perhaps. Go on one of those friendship tours, or whatever they call them. I'm sure we could manage for a few weeks without you, Emmie, and it's quite a good way for lonely people to have a little fun. Who knows, you might even meet someone who is in the same boat as you, and——'

'I am *not* in need of a friendship tour,' interrupted Emmie firmly, because she couldn't bear the implication behind Lissa's well-meant suggestion. 'And what's more, I am not going to sell it.'

'Not sell it?' Melissa blinked. 'Then what in heaven's name are you going to do with it?'

'Run it.'

'Run it! My dear, you can't be serious?'

'I am serious.' Emmie met her elder sister's eye unwaveringly. 'I was never more serious in my life.'

'Now look here, Emmie, it doesn't do to be too hasty about these matters.' Mark's brows drew together in a scowl, and his voice took on that considering, lawyer-like weightiness which it often did when he was dispensing a piece of reasoned advice. 'One has to consider all the angles before making a decision like that. One can't just decide on the spur of the moment, before you can even say "snap-crackle-and-pop".'

'One can, and I have,' Emmie corrected him gently. Her eyes were wide and round, shining with excitement. 'Just think of it, a dear little shop in the country! I'll love it! One of those ones with a bell on the door, that rings every time as people go in and out, with neat shelves of gleaming tins, and jars of sweets, and the regular customers coming in every day for their papers. I'll get to know them all by name quite soon, I'm sure. I'll get to have lots of friends. I was beginning to, down at the library, as a matter of fact—getting to know the regulars, I mean.'

'Huh!' Sharon gave a strangled grunt of disbelief. 'Darling, Mark is right, you know, when he says it simply isn't on. I mean, for a Montfort to be even thinking of running some wretched little shop in some dull, provincial little country town. And have you thought—those regular customers aren't going to be like the *library* ones, you know. They're bound to be a lot of country hicks. *Hayseeds*.'

'And what about us, and the house?' put in Robert. 'Who'd keep things going properly here? No, it's out of the question, Emmie, and you know it. If you'd stop to think for a bit, instead of getting all wide-eyed with wonder, you'd see that you can't even contemplate it.'

'You don't really need me, any of you,' she replied calmly, striving not to allow her assurance to be shaken by their concerted opposition, which she should have known to expect by now. 'Only for the things I do in the house, and a reliable daily could do those chores for you just as well as me. Better, probably. No, *none* of you needs me, Robert—not in the way that those poor children do. You, being a doctor, and working with children all the time, can surely see that?'

'My *dear* Emmie'—Mark sounded as though his patience was threatening to come to an abrupt end—'there's absolutely no obligation upon you to continue to harbour those *children*.' The mere idea seemed to astound him. 'Miss Millicent hadn't even adopted them, she was only fostering them, just to do a favour to the Far-Out Homes. There's a definite difference, you know—a clear-cut, *legal* difference, between the responsibilities of adoption and those of merely fostering. A foster-mother can opt out at any time.'

'Millie didn't *mean* to opt out, though, did she?' argued Emmie—quite hotly, for her. 'She was *taken*, and very suddenly indeed! Just think of the shock to those poor little things. One minute they had a happy home and a—a loving foster-mother—and the next they hadn't. It's unthinkable that I should let them down, and I have a feeling they must have been in Millie's mind when she left me the business. She may or may not have had a premonition, but at least she could reasonably suppose that, if anything happened to her and I stepped into her shoes at the shop, I'd also step into her role as foster-parent to those poor children. Millie knew what we *all* know——' She looked them firmly in the eye as she said this. 'Millie knew well enough that I haven't anything really worthwhile to do with my life, that I've got no gifts or talents, that I'm never likely to get married or do anything particularly exciting in the way of a career. She knew just what she was doing, in fact, because now she has given me the very thing I was never likely to have—a role to play, something worthy to do.'

'Worthy? A tiny little shop at the back of beyond?' Sharon scoffed.

'The shop is incidental, as Millie meant it to be. It's the children that are the worthy cause—giving them a good start, continued security and happiness and fun, like Millie meant them to have. And Koolonga isn't at the back of beyond, Sharon, and full of country hicks. It's right on the railway line.'

'Well, what about *us*?' There was a wailing chorus of protest all about her as her family finally realised that gentle Emmie was indeed in earnest, that she meant what she said, however crazy it was.

Emmie had had to maintain that firmness right to the end, right to the very moment when she climbed into the train at Central and waved them all a relieved and exhausted goodbye.

It had been difficult not to allow herself to be overridden by their alternate scoldings and entreaties, but at twenty-six one *had* to have a mind of one's own. At twenty-six, and with 'no prospects', one *had* to begin to stand on one's own feet, hadn't one? It was all very well, the way they had all carried on, but it was only a matter of time before Mark would bring a bride to the family home, and then he wouldn't want two women in the house at all. And Robert was already engaged and had hopes of a flat that went with the new consultancy. As soon as he got that, his own wedding arrangements would be going ahead. And Melissa's children would one day be too big to need a maiden aunt to keep an eye on them, just as the Montfort family themselves had outgrown the need for Miss Millicent. And Sharon had so many boy-friends that, by all the rules, she was one day bound to stop juggling them all around in that wasteful manner—(Emmie could have done with just *one* of them, quite splendidly!)—and settle for a permanent partner in life.

And what would become of her *then*? Emmie asked herself realistically, as the train rattled through Sydney's outer suburbs and on to Parramatta. What would become of her *then*?

It was still rattling on, that train, many many hours after Emmie had asked herself that question. It had been an unexpectedly tiresome and lengthy journey, and it was not yet over. The day had been a gruelling one—of heat and tiny flies that gathered around when she opened her sandwich lunch, and crawled on her bare arms, and tickled her neck; of crying babies, and fretful children who fell over her feet every time they went in and out of the compartment with that restless energy that the very young seem to reserve for long train journeys.

Now it was rattling away again, but this time it was on a branch line. The light was rapidly fading, and she was alone in the carriage.

Emmie had not realised that, about the branch line. When she had glanced over the map to find Koolonga, it had been enough simply to see that the dot which marked the town was firmly placed on the black, broken line which meant a railway. The map had not said that the railway line was a branch one, although Emmie supposed that if she had taken more trouble when looking, she would have noticed the fact for herself. Neither had the map indicated that only two trains a week ran on this particular branch line, or that they were somewhat antiquated motor-trains. Emmie had had to find that out at Berroola Junction away back there, and now here she was, seemingly the only passenger in this second-last carriage, although there were probably a few other people scattered about through the train's other two coaches.

If there were other passengers, she had lost interest in the fact, she was bound to admit. Her curiosity had become dulled, replaced now by a creeping lethargy which had to be fought off with determination in case it engulfed her altogether. There had been a lot to attend to prior to her departure, and the family, as usual, had prevailed upon her to do a lot of last-minute errands and chores. Now she was too hot, too sticky, too hungry, too weary, to worry very much about what the other passengers on this train were feeling, or even to wonder if there were, in fact, any other passengers at all.

Perhaps I've been crazy, she thought, and then pushed the thought away half-fearfully as a couple of kangaroos straightened high, ears alert, and stood quite still with their paws poised over their furry tummies as the train lurched past over the flat brown plain. Maybe Mark had a point. She buried that niggling uncertainty, watched instead as a giant, ungainly bird that could only be an emu loped off helter-skelter into a sea of yellow-blossomed scrub with an oddly drunken, lopsided gait. Could Robert's caution have actually been warranted? She dismissed the mere possibility, followed with her eyes the screeching flock of pink and grey parrots that sheered low over the stunted vegetation and disappeared in a shimmering wave into the rosy dusk of the setting sun.

Sandy watercourses threaded an arid path over the plains; lonely, broad plains that brought that tiny flutter of apprehension to Emmie's throat again. She wished that she had taken a larger flask. Her tea had been finished long ago, and her mouth felt as dusty and dry as those channel-beds out there where the turpentine bushes and drab myalls sucked away the moisture from below the soil surface in their fight for continuing survival. In the gold-fired glow of sunset a windmill loomed dark on the horizon. Beside it was an earth-walled tank, and a galvanised iron hut. A dwelling of some sort, perhaps. And a dwelling meant human beings, didn't it?

Emmie had been getting a little bit worried about the dearth of human life as the train sped on its noisy way over the branch-line sleepers. Apart from a drover's outfit, with a sulky and some dogs and a skinny youth on horseback tailing some spares at the rear of a vast mob of questing sheep, there only seemed to be animals and birds in evidence just now. The dignified grey kangaroos, those lolloping emus that galloped away in such an ungainly fashion, those screeching flocks of brilliantly coloured parrots, all appeared to be heading the same way as Emmie and the little motor-train, right into the rosy, diffused haze of the west. They couldn't go much further without getting back to a more civilised landscape, could they? After all, she was going to Millie's *shop*, and shops meant towns. Koolonga couldn't be more than another half-hour's journey, if she were to believe what the man at Berroola Junction had told her.

Emmie leaned back against the sticky warmth of her seat, and tried to imagine the sort of place that Miss Millicent would have chosen in which to retire. She had been an en-thusiastic gardener, Millie. A lover of green lawns and shrubs and trees. She had often talked of the small cottage she would one day like to have, in a pretty little country valley, with white walls and a purple wistaria climbing over the porch. She would grow roses, she'd said. And she would have beds of agapanthus and white lilies, and at the bottom of the garden she would have an apricot tree, because Miss Millicent had always said that apricots were her favourite fruit, and that you hadn't really tasted one to proper advant-age unless you had just picked it, warm and fully ripe, directly from the tree upon which it grew.

Emmie could do with an apricot right this minute.

She thought of its succulence and its warm, sharp juice with a fervour that was also tantalising. She was still think-ing about it when the noise of the motor subsided and the train slowed to a grinding stop. Heavy steps sounded outside and then her carriage door was wrenched open and a man leaned in.

'Was you the dame th't wanted Koolonga? If you are, here she is.' He was the driver of the train. Brief and laconic.

Emmie stared. She hadn't nodded, actually, but he seemed to accept the stare as an affirmative, because he was already pulling down her cases and slinging them out through the door.

'Koolonga? Are you sure?' She tried to peer beyond the

17

man's shoulder, but all she could see was a small piece of platform, a tiny slatted shed that looked like a signal-box, a wedge of faded rose that was the evening sky and the tracery of a pepper tree that showed up like black lace against the cloudy pink beyond.

The man grinned. It was a slow grin. Wry. Amused.

'Sure I'm sure. I reckon I've been doing this run since before you was a nipper, even. That's her. Koolonga.'

He swiped her luggage together and clambered down.

'Oh, please, watch how you carry that! It—they're my hats, you see. I didn't know how else to pack them.' Emmie tumbled out after him and retrieved the large paper bag, peeped in to reassure herself that the contents were unharmed. The man's grasp, after all, had been careless and excessively casual, and his hands were large and rough. Greasy, too.

'Where d'you reckon you're going to wear *them* things? You got a wedding lined up, or is it a bush christening?'

He smiled good-naturedly and ambled away in the direction of the little slatted shed.

It *was* a signal-box, and he was already busy changing the staff and pulling levers. Apparently he had forgotten his erstwhile passenger already.

'Excuse me——' Emmie had thrown down the paper bag containing her hats upon the rest of her piled-up luggage with a reckless haste that must have appeared somewhat illogical, considering that she had just reprimanded the man for his own carelessness with these selfsame articles. Luckily he wasn't looking.

'Excuse me——' she panted, hurrying after him as he shut the signal-box door and headed once more towards the motor-cabin. 'Please—where *is* Koolonga itself?'

'Right here, miss, like I said. Look.' He pointed a stubby finger at the neat white board with its black printed title. KOOLONGA, it read, without a doubt. 'Koolonga Siding, see.'

The few other passengers already had their heads out of

the windows, querying the delay.

'Yes, but——' Emmie smiled a little desperately. 'The—er —the town itself?' she suggested nervously but determinedly. 'Where is that?'

The man scratched his head, in genuine perplexity this time.

'Well, I mean, it's *there,* ain't it—if yer like to call it a town. Like I said, it's Koolonga *Siding,* see. But there's a store down there. It ain't in use just now, though. Beyond that there's a couple of petrol pumps and a telephone. The Bradys run the Post Office, an' the school's over the other side of the level crossing. You'll see them better once I go.'

Once he *went*! My goodness! Once he *went* there'd be nobody here at all. Just Emmie and that neat white noticeboard.

She felt stunned at the mere thought. She wanted, suddenly, to cry out, Please don't go. You can't go and leave me here alone, can you?

But he could, and he did.

Her words hadn't come. They were still unspoken, mere pleadings in Emmie's strangled throat, as he turned and climbed up into his cab with a 'thumbs up' sign that sent the few heads disappearing inside the windows again. A moment later the small train had gathered speed once more, and Emmie stood right where she was, and watched it snaking away over the plain until it was no more than a little black worm wriggling into the distance.

Once the worm had quite gone, she turned and looked about her.

Up and down the small platform.

It sloped away gently at either end, slipping unobtrusively back into the monotonous, tussocky plain again. The cemented edge of the platform was neatly painted white, to show the demarcation between platform and railway line. The paling fence that ran along behind the gravel length of it was white too, but the signal-box itself sported a rather less recently applied coating, of a dirty caramel colour. On either side of the board which spelt out 'Koolonga' there was a half-mooned flower bed, cluttered with perennial geraniums. They and the pepper tree drooped in the evening gloom, cowering in sagging submission to a sun that had beaten down on them relentlessly all through the day.

They looked defeated. Wilted. Emmie experienced a kindred twinge of sympathy. She felt that way herself!

The railway gates defended the approaches of a dusty track, worn and rutted and tyre-marked. Heaven knew where it came from, that road, but it undoubtedly led to the few scattered buildings to which the train-driver had pointed in the gloaming. After sidling around the buildings' precincts, it wound away again.

Emmie picked up her two heavier cases, and made for those gates. She opened and closed each one as she crossed the line.

She was panting with effort by the time she reached the veranda of the store, and her shoulders ached agonisingly. Most of Emmie's possessions were in those two cases. They, together with the third one back there on the platform, plus her rug and the hats and the small plastic picnic case, comprised her 'worldly goods', she reminded herself breathlessly, as she took the single shallow step up on to the veranda.

Above the step, in the fading light, she was able to distinguish the sign which proclaimed the place to have once belonged to 'Laceys, General Merchants'. Beneath, less obscurely, was printed Millie's own name.

'Miss J. Millicent, Owner.'

Well, that left no doubt, did it? Emmie felt the last faint hope that she could possibly have come to the wrong place die a brief, sore death within her.

This was it, quite certainly. The venture for which she had thrown up her safe existence, those dubious city comforts, the pallid satisfaction of anonymous security in the bosom of her brilliantly successful family. She had sustained her determination to come, in the face of so much vehement opposition, because some inner, inexplicable instinct had told her that at last, through Miss Millicent's final will and testament, she was about to find a new and exciting approach to life itself. New, because she was going somewhere where she was needed, quite badly, in a way in which Mark and Robert and Lissa and Sharon could never need her. Exciting, because Millie had always painted her dipping, green valley that way. She had drawn her little white-walled house and her roses and her apricots with such consummate skill and vividness that the picture had come alive. It lived with a reality that was tantalising and inviting—magical, almost.

Emmie put down the cases upon the decaying boards, blinked away the disappointment that at this moment threatened to demoralise her entirely, and turned resolutely back to where the remainder of her belongings lay awaiting transportation.

Her despair was such that she pushed the bulging hat-bag feverishly beneath one arm, slung the rug along with it, seized the picnic holdall and the last of her heavy suitcases, and dragged her unwilling feet back through the dust to the front of Miss Millicent's general store. Or rather, her *own* general store. Emmie's.

She gazed at her dubious inheritance with a mute disbelief that widened her hazel eyes into great, perplexed pools in the pale oval of her small, dusty, perspiring face. The weight of that luggage, the trek unaided with her burdens, had brought a dew to Emmie's forehead that had eventually channelled its way from her temples right down to her neck, her collar.

She could see the outline of her own form reflected in the glass of the cobwebbed windows, but only the outline, not the travel-stained details. Emmie was thankful for that! If she looked as drained as she felt, the picture was bound to be a depressing one, and anyway, the view beyond her mirror-image was enough to send her spirits floundering, in a final sinking spiral, right to the pit of her stomach.

Hands on either side of her eyes to shut out the last of the twilight reflections, Emmie could only stare through the glass. She felt so numb, so weary, that it was difficult to accept the reality of those dusty counters, drab shelves, dingy curtains, the disordered piles of stock so jumbled, so chaotic, so—so absolutely *antiquated*—that it was like peering back into another century.

Oh, Millie! Whatever could have brought you *here*? Where was the lush green valley, the little white-walled house, the porch with its scramble of wistaria? Where were the roses, and the apricot tree, and all those other promised things? Where, come to that, were the *children*? Not here, certainly. Here there was only emptiness and desolation. Creaking floorboards and fly-stained curtains. Filthy windows and mouse-plagued counters. Powdery cobwebs. Spidery graveyards, beaded with the bodies of small, dead flies.

Emmie shuddered.

The front door refused to yield. She made one or two effete attempts upon the windows themselves, and then walked slowly around to the back.

The building had a weatherboard lean-to attached to the rear. Surprisingly, the door-handle turned obligingly beneath her fingers, and Emmie stepped inside, into what must obviously be the kitchen. A bedroom lay to her right, a bathroom to her left. The bathroom had the usual plumbings, and a tiny, dim window. Most of the floor space was occupied by a gigantic iron-legged bathtub and a monstrous-looking geyser whose dragon-like, open mouth revealed the remains of what had presumably been its last meal—a mound of white mulga ash and some half-burnt, crumpled papers.

She shut the door, inspected a second bedroom and the familiar spectacle of the store itself.

At close quarters, and in this gloom, it was an oddly pathetic sight. Difficult to associate it with the prim and orderly Miss Millicent. There had to be an explanation, though. A reason for its deserted state, and for the absence of those foster-children, too. But right now Emmie was too dazed, too low, even to conjecture.

She unlocked the front door, stepped out into the warm night air, and pulled her cases inside. Her fingers sought automatically for the electric switch, found none. No light, even. And it was rapidly becoming quite dark. She quelled her growing uneasiness at the realisation of her predicament, dismissed the idea of going further down the road, to the Post Office or the school. If no one happened to be in either of those places, she'd have missed the last of the light. Better to install herself for the night, while she could still see what she was doing, at least. In the morning she'd have to take stock of things. She'd have to *think*. Just now, it was better not to think too deeply at all, because it might only serve to increase the hollow misery that had formed itself into a hard, unyielding ball at the base of her throat. Just now, it was better simply to concentrate upon doing things, one by one. Things like finding some means of lighting the place, and boiling a kettle to make herself some tea. Tea would do to wash down the two curling sandwiches that remained from her picnic lunch. Then she must make up one of those canvas-ticked stretchers upon which to sleep. Oblivion would be welcome. It couldn't come quickly enough, so far as Emmie was concerned! She was giddy with fatigue and reaction. Not even her corroding anxieties at the mess she had got herself into could be allowed to postpone that longed-for oblivion. Thinking was *definitely* for the morning—and yet, in spite of herself, thoughts kept on coming, just the same.

There was no going back! The memory of Sharon's mocking eyes, of Mark's predictable 'I told you so,' were enough to send her scurrying for some matches.

She found them, a whole carton of them, upon one of the dusty shelves. Her fingers fumbled as she lit a small lamp, turned up the wick, and carried it back to the kitchen.

There was a large black range against the outer wall, but no wood with which to set it going. On the table she espied a single-ringed kerosene cooker. It would do to make a cup of tea, at any rate.

It had a fat belly which gurgled appreciatively as she poured into it some fuel which she had found beneath the sink. Emmie returned the can to its place, and toyed tentatively with the pressure-pump on the cooker's bulging side. In the absence of instructions, she gave it several half-hearted plunges until she felt some slight resistance building up inside, and then gingerly relinquished the lever.

It was with some trepidation that she struck a match, turned the knob to its 'on' position, and cupped her hand over the sputtering wax taper as she guided it towards the small, hissing circular ring at the top. The next second there was a blinding flash, a single spurt of blue flame which licked the side of her cupped left palm before it died away to nothing, leaving Emmie clutching her stinging hand between her knees as she gritted her teeth against that instant, searing pain. It was so briefly agonising that it took a certain measure of will-power to let go her tight grasp of one hand upon the other, and turn off the knob again, but she had the presence of mind to do it. She was just congratulating herself upon the fact, when heavy steps sounded through the front room, followed by a muffled curse as their owner came in contact with what must probably have been a piece of furniture. The contact was sufficiently forceful to send whatever it had been flying to the floor with a resounding crash.

There was a renewed curse, then the doorway was blocked by a man's large frame, and an irate voice barked out of the dimness:

'What in blazes do you think you're doing, might I ask?'

CHAPTER TWO

Emmie put her injured hand behind her back, and stared.

'I might ask you the same thing,' she retorted with dignity, masking her fright with a certain coldness, 'since this happens to be my shop.'

'You——? Did you say *your* shop?'

The man lifted the lantern and played it over her face carefully and deliberately.

He was a tall man, as tall as Mark, and as powerfully built. He had a leanness, though, a sort of agile, whippy strength, that neither of her brothers possessed. It was an almost animal quality, with its own distinct physical impact. Careless, yet graceful, in the way in which a panther is graceful. In the pool of light his build was impressive, almost menacing, and not for the first time in her life, Emmie found herself longing for the advantage that some extra inches might have given her. It was humiliating to find one's heart pounding with alarm in this suffocating way, just because one had been unexpectedly confronted by a long, lean, broad-shouldered, sun-browned stranger with an angular, square-jawed face that was of a colour akin to the shell of a walnut. At this moment, cragging brows were drawing together over the levellest grey eyes that Emmie had ever seen in her life. Beneath the eyes was an imperious nose, a somewhat unremitting mouth. She couldn't see his hair, because it was concealed beneath a slanting, broad-brimmed hat which he hadn't bothered to remove. The hat was a rather battered khaki felt affair, and she supposed the hair which it hid would be black and abundant, to match those sun-streaked, dark brows.

The man raised the lantern further aloft, and in the shifting beam the action caused a ripple of sinew and muscle in the arm which was revealed beneath the carelessly rolled sleeve of a soiled bush-shirt.

It was obvious that here was a man in the peak of condition, compared with say Mark, or Robert, both of whose sedentary occupations meant that their most onerous physical exertion was likely to be no more than a snatched game of golf at the week-end, or a sail around Middle Harbour.

The stranger before her was a manual worker of some sort, judging by the tautness of those hardened muscles, and the supple stance of his shabbily clothed form. His narrow moleskin trousers were faded and worn; his elastic-sided boots were caked with dust.

She raised her eyes to find that his own were scanning her face curiously. They were half-closed, speculative grey slits in his tanned, weathered face, and there were deeper lines grooving out from their corners. Lines, too, running from the slightly aquiline nose to the corners of that disapproving mouth.

Emmie looked away.

'Did you say—*your* shop?' he prompted again, and Emmie lifted her eyes from those dusty boots with their defined, stockman's heel, and brought them back to the weathered face where the intent, waiting eyes were demanding an answer.

'*My* shop,' she repeated firmly, drawing herself up to her full height, which was still miserably insignificant. The action did little more than bring her nose level with the middle button of the man's double-pocketed khaki shirt.

'How come?'

He appeared unimpressed.

Well! What a creature! Admittedly, she was an unremarkable figure herself, wasn't she, and it wasn't *much* of a shop, was it, but you'd think he'd have had the grace to appear just a little more interested—apologetic, even, since he had marched in through her own front door and frightened the life out of her!

He didn't, though. His features remained unrevealing as he put the lamp down on the table beside the cooker, groped in his pocket for tobacco and papers, leaned back against the sink, and began to roll himself a cigarette.

His fingers went about their ritual with a dexterity which somehow fascinated Emmie. She withdrew her gaze again with difficulty.

'It's mine because Millie—Miss J. Millicent—left it to me,' she announced, irritated at that off-hand manner, his seemingly complete indifference.

'I *inherited* it,' she insisted, more forcibly.

'The devil you did!' The man's square-tipped fingers paused in the very act of bringing the newly fashioned cigarette to his lips. He became suddenly very attentive indeed! 'What is your name, please?'

'Emmie—I mean, *Emily*. Montfort,' she added in a defensive mumble, wondering why on earth she should suddenly find her own words lacking in conviction. Why, goodness, it almost sounded as if *she* were the apologetic one!

'Are you sure you are telling the truth—about that inheritance?' The grey eyes raked her in a puzzled, and puzzling, way. 'You're just a child——'

'*Hardly*.' Her mouth quivered at that. With amusement at his remark. With helplessness, frustration, bewilderment, too.

In a way he was right about that. She felt as uncertain as a four-year-old, and she was too light-headed with weariness and that smarting pain in her hand to contradict the man's statement with any real authority. 'Look, would you p-please go?'

Emmie saw his rugged features tighten visibly.

'I'm not leaving you here like this. You'll have to come with me.'

'I'm staying here,' she said flatly, without defiance. 'If you knew what I've gone through to get here, you wouldn't even suggest a thing like that!'

27

'I'm not *suggesting*,' the man corrected her with a certain level emphasis. 'It's an order.'

An order! Just who did he think he was, this dusty-booted, teak-brown stranger with the proud bearing that even a liberal coating of dust and grime could not conceal? Who was he, to think he had the authority to order her out of her very own store, ramshackle though it might be!

Emmie had a sudden weak desire to giggle. She wanted to laugh at her own tenacity in clinging to the wish to remain here, when only minutes earlier she'd have given anything to see another human being, not to mention being offered an alternative to this lonely, desolate accommodation for the night. That, minutes ago, would have seemed little short of a welcome miracle! And now here she was, turning down the positive offer of that very thing. It must be the man—something about him—that caused this sudden contrariness in Emmie, this uncharacteristic compulsion to assert her independence.

'One doesn't just go off into the night with any odd man who might happen along,' she rebuked him primly.

'Not any man. Fenton's the name. *Riddley* Fenton. So now that we know each other'—his mouth lifted sarcastically —'get your things together like a good girl, and we'll be going.'

'I've no intention of going, thank you.' Emmie's voice cooled. 'So far as I'm concerned, you *are* any man, just like I said. The name Fenton means absolutely nothing to me.'

'No?' One mobile brow lifted in seeming amusement at that. 'Well, if it doesn't now, it will shortly. That is, if you are in fact who you claim to be?'

'Look here, are you suggesting——'

'I'm suggesting nothing.' He sounded weary, suddenly near the end of his patience. 'I don't make *suggestions* at this hour of the night—not after a heavy day's scrub-cutting and a long drive on top of it. I save my breath for necessities, and if I have to, I give orders. What's more, I expect them to be carried out—*promptly*,' he added tersely, and then, his expression sharpening, 'What have you done to that hand?'

'It's nothing.'

'I'll be the judge of that. Let me see.'

The man placed the remaining inch or so of cigarette between his lips for safe keeping, stepped forward, and grasped her arm. Then he moved the lamp nearer and turned her palm upwards, squinting at it through a wreath of smoke.

'You burnt it?' Riddley Fenton reached beyond her to the sink, stubbed out his glowing butt with careful precision, and returned his eyes to her hand. 'When?'

'Just now. I was trying to light that little stove. I don't know much about them, so I suppose I did the wrong thing. I was just going to try again when—when *you* came in.'

He ignored the censure which was all too evidently linked with his intrusion, gave a non-committal grunt through closed lips, and continued to inspect the injury.

Her hand lay upturned in his. It looked small and pale against his own tough, brown palm. Small and pale and— vulnerable.

Emmie made to withdraw, and his grasp tightened. The pressure made her wince, even though he had not meant to hurt her.

'Hold still.' He frowned. 'It's quite extensive, and I'm afraid it's going to blister. Is it very sore?'

'Not very. I hardly feel it.'

The man's lips twisted as he released her hand at last.

'The martyred type, as well as stubborn,' he remarked nastily, retrieving his hat, which he had thrown carelessly on to the kitchen dresser, and turning her way once more. 'I'll dress it for you when we get home, and that will ease it a bit. And'—the grey eyes glinted dangerously—'if you're thinking of arguing, don't.'

There was something in the way he said that last bit which, together with the glint, told Emmie that, whatever she felt, it might in the end be wiser to obey. To tell the truth, anyway, she was too terrified of that little kerosene cooker to try it again just now, and wherever he was taking her, she might at least get that longed-for cup of tea! Her mouth felt dry, her throat parched. If she got a cup of tea out of the excursion, the hand could take its own chance!

'I'll get your gear. Go out and wait in the jeep.'

'You mean——'

'I mean just exactly what I say.'

'But aren't I coming back tonight?'

'Most certainly not. Now, just obey for once, will you, Miss Montfort? It would make a pleasant change.'

Emmie bit her lip, but refrained from replying. She was too exhausted to think of anything particularly clever, and he was proving to be quite a *formidable* intruder, as it turned out. One would need to be in tip-top form to hold one's own, and at the moment she was far from that.

She had just scrambled into the jeep when the sight of Riddley Fenton hauling her luggage outside and pulling the front door shut behind him sent her flying forth again.

'Oh, please be careful of that! That one there!' She rescued the large bag which he had been on the very point of tucking under his arm along with one of the cases. 'They—they're my hats, you see.'

She opened the bag to show him.

He peered obediently inside in the semi-dark, but 'Good God!' was all he said. However, he left the bag to her own ministrations after that, slung her cases one by one into the back of the vehicle and held open the passenger door, after which he got in at his own side and drove away without speaking again.

He seemed to be lost in thought. By the dim light of the dash she could see his profile, swarthy, absorbed, his eyes unreadable hollows above the faintly aquiline nose, the level mouth just now pursed consideringly, as if he had a problem. He drove fast, the yellow beams of the jeep's headlights searching out the road ahead with unerring skill, avoiding ruts and bumps as they came into view, swinging in and out of belts of timber and stands of lower scrub.

30

'Wh-where are we going?' Emmie hesitated to disturb his reverie, but she had to know, didn't she?

He glanced her way, then back to the road again.

'To Koolonga.'

'I thought we were *at* Koolonga. Back there. Is this the town we're going to?' She didn't mean to sound hopeful, but she was!

'There's no town at Koolonga. It's just a siding. Presumably, as you got off there, you must have known that already. Or didn't you bother with the customary preliminaries and take the precaution of finding out where you were coming to before you left your own neck of the woods—wherever that was?' His eyes rested lingeringly upon the hat-bag which she was preserving carefully upon her lap.

'Sydney,' she informed him abruptly, hating the silken thread of sarcasm that was woven into his words. 'And yes, of *course* I did. I—I was just—er—curious, that's all,' she added lamely.

She was at enough of a disadvantage already without admitting her folly openly. She could just imagine how his lip would curl, how heartily he'd laugh at her, if he could only guess how built-up she'd been this morning, and how deflated she felt right now!

'We are going to Koolonga *Station*,' he informed her, with a sort of exaggerated patience, as if as aware of her ignorance as she was herself. 'That's where I live. We're nearly at the homestead now.' Another sidelong glance. 'Is that hand still giving you gyp?'

'It's not bad. Tell me——' She changed the subject a little tremulously, because her hand *was* extraordinarily painful, as it happened. 'Tell me, what is scrub-cutting? Wasn't that what you said you'd been doing?'

'That's right. And it's just exactly what it says. Scrub-cutting. The cutting of scrub to feed hungry stock. Just like the poet said, although it's far from poetic work, believe me— "All day we had driven the starving sheep, to the scrub where the axes ply." '

He quoted the line wryly, but with a singular lack of amusement all the same.

'You mean—you cut the—the *trees*?'

He nodded.

'They'll eat anything we can give them in the way of non-poisonous greenery when they're starving, Miss Montfort. So would you, if you'd had as little to pick up as they have this past six months,' he replied somewhat grimly. 'It's bad when it gets down to this. The cattle are off, and half my sheep stock are agisting on a couple of my other places. The rest are still taking their chance here as yet. I'm gambling on some rain before too long.' The broad shoulders shrugged philosophically. 'I'm luckier than some, in having properties in better areas to send them to. It's hell to be overstocked in a season like this one. It can break a man if he's caught with no alternatives. Some poor devils are forced to sell out for whatever they can get, and that can include their breeding stock, their flock ewes. For others——' Again the shrug. 'Well, the stock routes are jammed with travelling mobs just now. You probably saw some from the train, if you were looking out. Back the other side, east of Berroola, the route runs parallel for a couple of miles. The long road.'

He had spoken those last words to himself, wearily, almost as if he had forgotten, temporarily, that he had a passenger at all. The lines at the sides of his mouth seemed momentarily more deeply grooved in the pallid glow that came from the instrument panel. He looked remote, forbidding.

'I think I did see one of the mobs you spoke of,' Emmie told him timidly, because it was obvious that the topic was somehow not a very pleasant one. 'I saw a big, dusty lot of sheep, and a horse-drawn cart, and some men on horses, too. They were going very slowly, just sort of browsing along.'

'They'd have been pushing them, all the same. They've got to achieve a certain mileage each day—a stage—but if the stock are in poor condition it can be quite a job moving them along.'

'Why bother to, then? Why not just let them stay where

32

it's greenest, where they like?'

'No, Miss Montfort, I'm afraid that wouldn't work out. As in almost every sphere of life, you'd get certain elements showing up. Greed, in this case. There'd always be some clever cove hogging the best patches for longer than he should. It's a public way, a stock route, and in fairness to all, they've got to manage it properly. Keep stock moving, notify adjoining proprietors, make room for the next chap.'

'Yes, I see what you mean.' There was a small silence, and then she plucked up courage to observe cautiously, 'Surely there's quite a lot of grass there, though, at the sides of this very track we're on right now. So why do you have to cut tr—er—scrub— for your animals, anyway?'

'No feeding there. Dry as tinder, and a fire risk into the bargain, I'm afraid that's all that can be said for that lot.' His lips twitched. 'You don't know much about the country, do you, Miss Montfort?'

Again his eyes slid towards that hat-bag, with a hateful sardonic glint that even the darkness couldn't hide. Emmie wished that she'd never shown him the contents, after all! She wished she hadn't *brought* them, those hats! They were quite ridiculous affairs, anyway, and if she *had* known, *had* guessed the sort of place to which she was coming, of course she'd have left them back there for Sharon or Lissa to dispose of somehow.

Not that they were the sort of things that were easy to dispose of, unfortunately. Much too distinctive.

Models, actually— because there was a certain standard of dressing which Montforts were naturally expected to maintain, even 'plain Jane' Montforts such as Emmie.

Just peeping into that bag brought certain recent occasions quite vividly to mind.

The shantung-baku, for instance. It had graced the last Spring Meeting at Randwick, an affair to which she had been dragged somewhat unwillingly by Robert and his girlfriend. And then, after their apparent sincerity in wishing for her company, they had shortly disappeared into the

33

crowd of racegoers, and Emmie had been left to fend for herself. Not that they had actually meant to *dump* her, she was sure. It was just that it never occurred to either of them that Emmie might not know as many people as they did themselves. Might not know *anyone*, in fact. Because after all, how did you get to know anyone when you hadn't got swept into the social swim when you were young, the way Lissa and Sharon had? How could you know people, when you simply hadn't been where the people were? No, it hadn't been enjoyable at all. In fact, far from being enjoyable, it had actually been an agonising outing for the shy Emmie, who knew no one. Everyone else appeared to know *everyone*. If they hadn't come with friends, they soon appeared to spot some, greeting them with loud cries of delight which Emmie wished she could copy. Only she couldn't see anyone to hail with whoops of joy as of long-lost friends well met. Not anyone. Ah, well. For Robert's sake she'd tried to pretend to an excitement she hadn't felt, but she'd arrived home wondering just where she fitted into the present scene when she hadn't derived even a modicum of pleasure from such a hallowed date on the fashion calendar. For the hundredth time she had asked herself where she fitted in, and for the hundredth time she had had to admit, reluctantly, that she didn't. She was as much a misfit in the gay, brittle social round as she was the odd one out in that clever, ambitious, good-looking family of hers.

The Randwick hat was badly squashed. Its shantung straw crown was quite hopelessly dented, in fact. And Emmie didn't mind a bit!

The blue feathered thing she'd worn at young Peter's christening was wrecked, as well—and, strangely, she didn't mind *that*, either.

Emmie's memories of that christening were of rush and haste and muddle and a singular lack of assistance in all she'd had to do. She had been left to cope with three-year-old Lorna *and* the preparation of the large reception that was to follow the ceremony, while Melissa—who should have been

34

doing at least one, if not both, of these things—posed graciously for the gossip-column photographers with her adorable new baby, handed him over to his nanny, and then moved languidly about amongst her guests in the pleasant certainty that someone else—(Emmie, of course)—was behind the scenes where she had been despatched, to deal single-handed with all the sordid necessities.

Emmie peeped surreptitiously into the bag again, smiled in spite of herself.

The bare patch amongst the feathery blue, the bit where the canvas backing showed, was the place where little Lorna had pulled out a whole handful of feathers while Emmie was busy cutting more sandwiches. It had seemed too silly for words to be standing at the kitchen table cutting crusts off loaves with *that* sort of a hat upon one's head, and so she'd removed it—unadvisedly, as it turned out!—and left it on a chair. Shortly after she had been scolded for pulling out the feathers, Lorna had poured a mug of raspberry drink right down the front of her white organdie party dress, and then Melissa had scolded Emmie herself for not keeping a better eye on the child.

No, the blue feather thing was no great loss.

And there was the cream jersey turban, just beneath it in the bag. It had survived all right so far, and so had the velveteen beret she'd worn to the Sunday lunch at the Golf Club. But that white tulle which Mark had insisted upon her getting when he took silk—heavens!—what a mess! First, the train-man at the siding had grabbed the bag unceremoniously right on top of where the tulle hat must have been. And then she herself must have crumpled it further when she'd tucked all her trappings under her arm so despairingly to take them down to the store. She'd been proud of Mark that day, though. Proud, really, to be a Montfort. He'd looked so handsome—a handsome, austere creature on that occasion, yet unusually congenial to his middle sister in his moment of triumph, and afterwards he'd taken the whole family, including Emmie, for a meal at that new place down on the water-front at Milson's Point, where the oysters had been quite superb, and——

'Here we are, then. Koolonga.'

The man's deep voice, sounding briefly at her side, brought Emmie out of her trance.

Koolonga.

Well, if it wasn't a town, it certainly gave the impression of one, or at the very least of a small village.

The jeep rattled over a ramp, and in and out amongst the dark, squared shapes of buildings and sheds. Corrugated iron roofs gleamed faintly in the moonlight. Presently they turned through white-painted gates into the blackness of a tree-ranked avenue, swept up a gravel drive to a brick portcullis.

It was impossible to see much of the surrounding precincts.

Emmie allowed herself to be helped out, and followed Riddley Fenton up the steps. At the top he removed his hat with one hand, opened a gauze-meshed door with the other, and stood aside, motioning to her to enter. Then he led the way again. Through a long, wide hall with a waxed wooden floor, over which his dusty cowhide boots echoed crisply, to a door at the end.

'The bathroom. I'll give you five minutes to clean up, and then I'll see to that hand.'

The mirror told Emmie why he'd led her straight there. She had had no idea that her face was all streaked and smudged like that !

Her eyes looked like smudges, too. Big, dark, round ones, in her unnaturally pale face. The pain in her hand was echoed in the large, hazel pools of her eyes. It was all she could do to allow the cold tap-water to play gently over the angry scarlet place where the flame from the kerosene cooker had licked. She examined it carefully after dabbing it with a small, clean towel. Superficial, as burns went, luckily. Nothing to worry about, though it was certainly going to blister, as the man had predicted.

36

Emmie combed her hair back into its obedient, silken sheen, and then went back to the hall.

The room they retired to was obviously Riddley Fenton's study. A sort of office-cum-sitting-room. It had deep leather chairs, a large roll-topped desk, a couple of handsome rugs on the pine boards, and maps and rain-charts strung around the walls. There was a box strapped to the wall, too. A type of cupboard. When he opened it, Emmie saw that it was full of medical supplies, all neatly labelled or numbered.

'Sit down, please.' He sounded frighteningly businesslike.

'I'd as soon stand.'

'Just as you like.' His shrug was patently indifferent.

Emmie stood.

It seemed to her that she stood for a very long time, while he dressed her seared palm.

For such big, tough, sunburnt, scrub-cutting hands, this man's were unexpectedly gentle. They worked carefully and economically, in an unhurried, capable manner. She kept her eyes fastened on them, because she had to look somewhere, and if she raised her eyes at all, his face got in the way. It was a slightly grim face, impersonal, absorbed, and it was very close to her own, which was why she felt more comfortable looking down instead of up.

Now the brown fingers were winding a bandage lightly over the soothing gauze pad they had put in place. Emmie watched them, mesmerised. Their movements were unhurried but constant. Continuous. They had quite a giddying monotony, the way the two things alternated. The brown hands. The white bandage. Brown, white. Brown, white. Round and round. Brown and white. All muddled up together in a strangely woolly way.

'Damn!'

The brown and white had gone. Now there was just an expanse of khaki instead. A khaki shirt? A shirt-front? And then even that disappeared, and there was simply nothing, nothing at all.

'Lean forward. Put your head right down. That's it.

37

You'll be all right in a minute.'

From somewhere quite far away, the words reached Emmie.

To her surprise, the voice that spoke them was behind, now, instead of in front.

When her world stopped revolving, she found herself to be sitting in one of the great leather chairs. Emmie had no idea how she could have got there, but there she was, undoubtedly, and the pressure of someone's fingers was keeping her head down near to her knees. The fingers must be Riddley Fenton's, she supposed, for there was no one else around, was there? She could feel the roughness of his thumb caressing the nape of her neck, but when she took a sighing breath he removed it forthwith, and she was able to sit up, somewhat shakily.

'Better?'

'I'm terribly sorry. I mean, I've never——'

'There's always a first time for everything, isn't there? I'd say you're clocking up a record of them, this trip. Drink this. It might help.'

'What is it?' She eyed the small glass doubtfully.

'A time-honoured bush remedy, but effective.' He smiled faintly, and the mockery crept back into his eyes. 'Come on, it won't poison you. I thought you were the sort who'd be game for anything.'

'What makes you think that?' She wasn't sure that she liked that observation. Not the way *he* said it. She didn't much like this disgusting, milky-white concoction, either, but she drank it nevertheless with mute obedience.

'Why do I think it? Those hats, maybe.' He sounded amused. 'It's a pretty far cry from where you'd wear hats like those to a place like Koolonga, I reckon. I suspect you didn't know, when you set out on this crazy, wild-goose chase of yours, that Koolonga actually *means* "out-of-the-way"? It's aboriginal, for somewhere that's remote.'

'*Not* a wild-goose chase,' Emmie corrected him, leaning back and pushing her hair away from her damp forehead. 'I came to the shop, remember. The store.'

'And now that you've seen it, you'll agree it's an impossible proposition for a girl like you.' The broad back was towards her, as he started replacing the things in the medical chest once more. 'I'll take you back to the train again, but you'll need to spend a couple of days here, I'm afraid. The next train's not till Thursday. By the look of you, though, the delay won't do you any harm. You can rest, and Mrs. Bexley will love nothing better than to cosset you in the meantime. She has a passion for spoiling the weak and helpless.'

Emmie sat up, stung by that bland statement. Indignation brought angry spots of colour to her wan cheeks.

'That's quite unfair, to say that, just because of how I was a minute ago!' she blazed angrily. 'You don't know the first thing about me, and I can assure you that I'm neither weak *nor* helpless. Just because you're a man, and ten feet tall, you think——' She broke off when she saw the beginning of the grin lifting the corner of his mouth, changed tack. 'I—I had quite a—a time getting away, as it happens,' she defended herself. 'A lot to do before I left. And then there was the long day's journey on top of it. And the train was hot. What's more, I hadn't bargained for some complete and utter stranger to come barging into my very own shop at the end of it all to give me the mother and father of all frights.'

'I apologise for that.' There was an odd expression in his eye as he turned to look over at her. 'But what would you have done in my place? That store's been empty for over three months, and I happen to know that it was supposed to be locked. When I saw a light flickering at the back, I reckoned maybe a swaggie had taken roost, and naturally stopped to investigate.' A pause. 'There's another reason for my interest, too, as it happens, Miss Montfort. A reason that gives me an additional right to investigate anything I might consider untoward. I happen to be the late owner's—the late Miss Millicent's—sole executor.'

Emmie knew that her colour must be receding as rapidly as it had come. Well, of all the *luck*! Wasn't it just typical of everything that came her way in life, that Millie had had to choose an interfering, overbearing tyrant such as this one to see her affairs to rights?

'What does that—er—entail, exactly? Being sole executor?' she asked cautiously.

Maybe it didn't amount to anything much. Just some of that impressive legal jargon that sounded a lot more important than it really was. Mark was forever coming across with terms like that, and she often had the feeling that he used them simply to impress the uninitiated. She had a sudden suspicion, right now, that this man was trying the selfsame trick!

If he was, he was being extremely subtle about it. You could tell that by the way in which the broad shoulders lifted, carelessly, with a hint of resignation almost.

'It entails comparatively little, I regret to say, so far as you are concerned. You saw the state of the store for yourself. A doubtful asset, Miss Montfort, but I shall do my best to dispose of it satisfactorily for you.'

'But I don't *want* you to dispose of it,' she pointed out despairingly. (He really seemed to be bent on getting rid of her, didn't he?) 'I'm—I intend to *run* it.'

'It isn't a going concern.' There was an instant shake, a very *positive* shake, of that dark, imperious head. He had finished with the medicine chest, and now he came across the room. There was a strange sense of purpose, of deliberation, about the way he put a hand upon either arm of her chair and leaned down, quite near, effectively making her a prisoner. Emmie could smell the dust on his clothing—an intermingling of leather and sweat and earth and the strange, unfamiliar, oily smell that was eucalypt, probably from the bushes he had been cutting all day. His nearness was disturbing, but he appeared quite unaware of the fact. Unaware that he *was* near. Unaware of *her*. His face was inscrutable as he looked down, his eyes calm and unreadable.

'It's not a going concern,' he repeated, neither pleasantly nor unpleasantly.

'I'll make it a going concern again,' she protested stubbornly.

There was silence for a time. Then——

'I don't think you quite understand, Miss Montfort. That store depended for its custom almost solely upon Koolonga Station and the Bruces over at Berroola. Give or take a few prospectors and railway fettlers, the odd well-sinker or drover or swaggie, *our* needs were its only source of steady revenue. When Miss Millicent died we transferred to the town, to the stores at the Junction. The will didn't come to light for about six weeks—that's why the place is in such an unholy mess. In the end Des Connolly, the mailman, found it in a boiled-sweet jar.' His mouth lifted. 'Miss Millicent had shown quite unusual resourcefulness and eccentricity in hiding the darned thing, as a matter of fact, and in the meantime—well, we had to keep our supplies coming. So the switch to Berroola Junction was the natural alternative. Admittedly, it's further away, but there are certain advantages—more choice, better quality——'

'I—I'd make sure there was a choice, that the quality was good.' Emmie's eyes were round with pleading. With bewilderment and shock, too. Her prospects of a livelihood depended upon the surrounding stations, depended on men like *this* one. It wasn't good news. Anything but! 'I'd see that you had plenty of choice, Mr. Fenton, truly I would. I—I'm—I'd——'

'Look, young 'un'—the man stood up straight—'right now I could do with a shower and some grub. I'll show you to your room, and you can join me for dinner in forty minutes. Mrs. Bexley will make up a bed for you while we eat. O.K.?'

As if sensing her disappointment at being fobbed off, Riddley Fenton smiled. It was the first time he had allowed that faint lift of the mouth to turn into a proper smile, of calculated charm and persuasion.

Emmie watched the wrinkles deepen at the corners of

those slightly mocking grey eyes, noted the way his teeth contrasted so whitely with the deep tan of his lean, swarthy cheeks.

'Yes, all right.' She smiled bleakly in return.

She felt helpless. It was obvious that the man didn't take her seriously at all. What could she do, or say, she wondered as she followed him silently to the room she was to have, to convince him that she *was* to be taken seriously? There was no going back for Emmie now. She had burned her boats back there in Sydney, very thoroughly indeed! There was no going back, that much was certain. She was here, and here she meant to stay.

Perhaps Riddley Fenton would be in a more amenable mood once he had showered and changed and got some food inside him. Maybe that would mellow him a little. She certainly hoped so!

He was, as it turned out, a pleasant if offhand host.

To tell the truth, Emmie scarcely recognised as that dusty, sweat-stained scrub-cutter the man who held her chair for her, and saw her seated with impersonal urbanity before taking his own place at the head of the long cedar table. His cheeks were no longer stubbled and begrimed, but freshly shaven, smooth. Emmie could catch the pleasant tang of the after-shave he had used. His hair was smooth, too, blacker than ever with the damp still lingering from his recent ablutions. He now wore a crisp white shirt, an unexpectedly rakish cravat knotted at his brown throat, and pale drill trousers supported by a narrow leather belt. The boots had been replaced by another, almost identical, pair—but these ones were buffed and shining. They had much the same polished gleam as the lovely cedar table at which they were at this moment sitting. The shining silverware was reflected tenderly against its mellow surface tall candlesticks, elegant cutlery, the waxen petals of that somewhat wistful little floral bowl in the very centre, all had their images echoed in the patina of the beautiful wood upon which they had been placed.

The room itself was shadowed, because the light was one of those old-fashioned, chained affairs that hung low right over the table itself, catching the diners in a small, round pool. She was aware that it was a long room, a dual-purpose one, evidently, like his office. The far end was taken up with chairs and sofas, bookcases and a long, carved chest. The fireplace was at that end, too, the grate at present empty, screened by a piece of tapestry-work on a wrought iron mount. It was of cavernous proportions, the fireplace. The type that would probably take whole logs at a time. It had a large brass fender in front, and a pair of handsome firedogs at either end. She could imagine how the flickering firelight must enhance the entire appearance of this room, and yet Emmie found herself wondering if there could ever be the need for a fire, out here? The night was uncomfortably warm, outside, and as she had walked along the veranda from the room which had been allotted to her, she had heard the thin, persistent whine of mosquitoes, the buzz of flies and buffing of moths against the fine gauze that enclosed the house. These were hot-country sounds, backed by the shrill of cicadas and grating of frogs at the creek. They fitted in, somehow, where the intimate crackle of logs in a hearth did not. It was strangely airless this evening, and difficult to imagine things otherwise.

Airless, but in the house at least, not oppressive as it must be beyond. It was a cool retreat, a labyrinth of tall-ceilinged passages and peacefully shadowed, quiet rooms, such as this one she was in now.

A fan revolved silently from the sideboard, and every time its rotation brought it opposite to where she sat, she could feel its welcome breeze sweeping over her face, lifting her fine silky hair each time it passed.

Emmie had not realised that she was so hungry.

The mutton stew was delicious, steaming, thick with vegetables. It was followed by a chilled lemon pie, light as air, and cream which she guessed must be tinned, but which was surprisingly good, all the same. She ate in silence, appreciatively.

The man was silent too. He handled his knife and fork with the same deft, economical movements as he had those medicaments back in his study. Emmie was aware that his eyes were upon her several times during the course of the meal, but each time she looked swiftly away. The sense of being watched did little to ease the overwhelming shyness she was experiencing at finding herself dining, of necessity alone with a man who was not only an utter stranger, but a somewhat baffling one at that. The room was enormous, unfamiliar. The man was unfamiliar too. Yet here they were, just the two of them in this great cavernous place, encircled in a small, cosy pool of light.

Emmie wasn't used to this sort of thing at all. Her fingers tightened nervously over the stem of her glass as she toyed with it, waiting for her host to finish. Should she be making conversation? she wondered. Or did he actually *prefer* silence? Observing his now remote, preoccupied manner, and the stern set of his rugged features, Emmie decided that he probably did.

'Well?' A slow grin leavened the sternness. 'After that detailed inspection, I reckon you ought to know me again, don't you? What were you doing? Weighing up the enemy?'

'What? Oh—er—I do beg your pardon!' He had suddenly turned his dark head and looked directly at her, and one eyebrow was lifting quizzically. Emmie blushed, startled.

'You were staring, Miss Montfort,' he accused blandly. 'Now, don't get coy and say you weren't, because that guilty blush betrays you.'

Riddley Fenton grinned, leaned back, and searched in his pockets for the makings.

'You have no objection if I smoke? We'll have our coffee down the other end of the room, I think. You might find it easier to relax down there in one of those chintz loungers. You're sitting in that chair like an affronted schoolmarm at the moment!'

44

Again the grin.

Emmie groped for something quelling to say, quite failed to come up with inspiration. Just as well, maybe. There was no doubt he was enjoying himself at her expense. No doubt that he was 'taking the mickey'.

She eased her stiffening back, forced her fingers to release the glass upon which they had been tensely curled, and to rest idly on the mellow table-top. He mustn't suspect quite how she was feeling, must he? He was Millie's sole executor, and she had yet to win a couple of points on that score, so he mustn't guess that this sort of fascinated awe he aroused in her was a possible chink in her armour. Emmie had to control her breathing with a mighty effort, in case the chink should widen into a positive crack. If it did, he'd be sure to spot it. He was that sort of man, she knew it instinctively.

He was still watching her calmly through a wreath of smoke, and not attempting to disguise the fact.

'There's a certain compelling fascination about a truly ingenuous blush, don't you think?' A sigh. 'I'm afraid few of the women of my acquaintance are capable of it any longer. It's a dying art, you know. Quite Victorian, but charming, nevertheless.'

'Do you think we could have that coffee?' Emmie choked the words out tightly. 'I'm thirsty. I was just about to make myself some tea, if you remember, when that wretched little stove blew up.'

'Yes, of course.' He stood up, helped her to her feet, looked down at her ironically with narrowing eyes. 'You know something? You've got me puzzled, little Miss Montfort. You're a contradiction in terms. First that transparent blush, quite fetchingly childish—and then an adroit red herring dropped neatly right across the conversational path. With quite a sophisticated little punch to it, too, telling me not to get personal.'

'I'm glad you got the message,' she returned with a creamily smooth inflection that matched his own. Drat the man! He seemed to bring out the worst in her. Emmie was never like this to people—not to ordinary people, that is! 'I mean,' she added appeasingly, forcing herself to sound more civil, 'we don't *have* to be personal, do we?'

'I'm afraid we do,' he corrected her soberly. 'For just a couple of minutes more, at any rate. You see, there's something I intend to ask you.'

'Yes?'

Emmie's eyes were round, waiting, fastened on his face enquiringly.

'Yes,' he confirmed—then paused. His own eyes were holding hers and she was conscious of the most curiously alert intentness lurking in their supposedly lazy grey depths.

'Yes,' he said again, quite firmly. 'I knew some Montforts once. It's a while ago now, but they weren't the sort of family one could readily forget. Mark and Robert Montfort. There were a couple of sisters, too—Melissa and Sharon. Does any of that ring a bell?'

It was so totally unexpected that, just for a moment, Emmie's poise threatened to desert her entirely.

'Should it?' How on earth had she actually managed that offhand shrug? Emmie would never know! 'It's a more common name than you'd think.'

Perhaps he hadn't noticed her sudden uncontrollable intake of breath before calmness supervened, or the way her eyes had widened before she'd dropped them quickly and picked up the coffee tray.

'Shall I pour?'

'If you like.'

Emmie ran her tongue over her lips. She *did* like! It would give her something to do, help to tide her over what had been a surprisingly bad moment!

She had passed it off all right, though, she was sure. He had made no further comment, had simply taken the coffee-tray from her and set it down upon a small round table. Then he had hitched his narrow-legged drill trousers, and had taken the chair opposite her own, stretching out his long frame comfortably.

Emmie poured, passed him the cup and saucer with a hand that she was pleased to see didn't tremble at all. It would have been too bad altogether if her family had succeeded in following her out here after all. Away out here, to Koolonga that in itself meant remoteness. It would have been the cruellest quirk of fate to find that she hadn't, after all, escaped from the politely raised brows, the exclamation— What, another sister, good gracious me. The unspoken comparisons were so odious, so humiliating. So easily avoided, too, if you simply weren't there to *be* compared. It would have been unbelievable, to come all these hundreds of miles, to Koolonga—the lonely, the out-of-the-way place of the aboriginals' own language—only to find those old familiar exclamations and innuendoes following one, waiting here for her at the end of her trek just as they had always been.

It would have prevented Emmie from emerging into the sort of person she knew she could be, if only her brilliant family had allowed her. Discovery would be so inhibiting. So *cramping*. So cramping, all over again!

She swallowed, a little miserably.

Surely it wasn't dishonest, to deny her wonderful, brilliant family just the teeniest mite, in the most harmless way imaginable? She wasn't actually hurting anyone by doing that, was she? Not them? Or him? Not *them*, anyway. The idea of Emmie having any positive effect upon her family, one way or the other, no matter what she did, was entirely ludicrous. They were all so self-sufficient, so wrapped up in their own lives, their careers, that she scarcely counted, did she?

As for *him*—well, one only had to encounter that lean, imperious, stern-mouthed approach, experience the impact of that domineering, overbearing personality, to know that it couldn't matter one jot to Riddley Fenton either. He was composed, self-sufficient, as self-assured as *they* were. A law unto himself. Quite invulnerable.

'Those other Montforts—er—when did you know them?'

She asked the question with simulated idleness, spooning

47

brown crystals into her coffee as she spoke, and cursing her inquisitive nature for not allowing her to leave things alone.

'Mark and I were at Varsity together. Different faculties, of course—he was Law, I was reading Engineering—but he was quite a chap. A big, powerful, handsome devil, and one of our best rugby forwards. Robert was younger, reading Medicine, if I remember. There were a couple of ravishing sisters, too, who used to come to our various social functions. Lissa and Sharon, their names were, as I've already told you, I think.'

Emmie stirred her coffee feverishly. Well, that was the Montfort family, all right, wasn't it? The Montfort family, as the world had always known it. She was safe enough, after all!

'Still no bell?'

'No bell,' she affirmed, but her voice was oddly husky.

'Funny that. I was studying you at dinner-time, and I'd have said there was a definite resemblance—to Sharon in particular. Not the colouring—Sharon was dark, of course—but the shape of the head, the set of the eyes, something about the bone-structure——'

'P-perhaps a far-out cousin?' Emmie muttered weakly. She wished she hadn't had to lie like that, wished she hadn't got herself into this unpleasantly equivocal position, wished he would *stop*.

'Now you're blushing again. Why?'

'You said they were—er—ravishing—the—er—Lissa and Sharon.'

'Well? What if I did? Oh, I get it.' His mouth lifted. 'How like a woman, not to let that one pass! Well, so they were, and there *is* a resemblance—but I've been reprimanded already for getting personal, haven't I, Miss Montfort?' The grin spread, quite nastily. 'Otherwise, if I *hadn't* already been reprimanded, I just might have risked adding that, with a little more self-assurance, a little more experience, a little more maturity, you could—— But no, I can see that I

48

embarrass you. Drink up your coffee like a good girl, and I'll get Mrs. Bexley to take over. You'll find her womanly conversation infinitely more to your liking, I dare say.'

He stood up, took her hand quite firmly in a cool, hard grasp, and drew her to her feet.

'We—we were going to talk,' she reminded him on a shaky breath. 'You *promised*. About the shop. You said we'd discuss it later. I—I *have* to *know*.'

'It can't be that important, child.'

'It is. Terribly.'

'Not tonight. You're tuckered out, all eyes and pallor still. We'll discuss it in the morning. But I wouldn't hold out any false hopes, if I were you.'

'What do you mean by that?'

She put a hand to the base of her throat in a flutter of anxiety. Apprehension—panic, almost—gripped her anew. If he wasn't prepared to let her have that store, she'd be literally homeless!

'Just that you'll have to allow yourself to be guided in this,' he replied levelly.

At the door he paused.

'It's easily seen that your inexperience covers a wider range than merely the male of the species, young 'un. Admitting the fact, even if only to yourself, would be a step towards that maturity I spoke of. Goodnight.'

'Goodnight.'

She managed no more than a hollow echo as he disappeared to summon his housekeeper.

CHAPTER THREE

In the morning Emmie woke early. No sound had disturbed her, or at least, not any of which she was particularly aware. Rather did she suspect that it was the strange stillness of the young bush dawn—the piccaninny daylight—that had aroused her by its very unfamiliarity. A great, wide, wondrous silence enfolded her as she lay between snowy linen sheets, marvelling at the utter absence of noise.

And then a chain rustled, a dog barked somewhere beyond the veranda, and as if that bark had been a prearranged signal, the dawn chorus began—a cacophony of sounds, growing with the filtering light itself. A cock began to crow, hens to cluck in tentative rebuke at being thus rudely disturbed. From the sliprails came the creak of sadlery, the chink of stirrup-irons, the soft snorting of horses through black velvet nostrils, the rattle of a milk-bucket, the protesting bellow of a cow being driven to the bail. Overhead, a rush of air, a crescendo of buffeting, beating wings, as a great flight of galahs swept low over the homestead in a pink and grey cloud, and a shrieking, twittering flock of lorikeets soared out of the box trees next to the stockyards, a vivid carpet of colour against the paling sky.

The big station—'Koolonga, the remote and lonely place' —was awake, and Emmie with it.

She slipped out of bed and padded barefoot along the veranda to the tiled bathroom at the end, managed a shower without wetting her bandaged hand. It was better this morning. The smarting pain had gone out of it, and she succeeded in buttoning up her blue-and-white checked dirndl without discomfort.

Emmie brushed her hair, touched her lips with pale rose

colour, decided against any more obvious efforts to make up. 'When in Rome.' Or rather, when in the *country*, do as the country people do. The trouble was, she hadn't any very clear idea of what they did do, or how they behaved. Quite suddenly she had found herself plunged into a totally unfamiliar world, and one that already seemed oddly full of contradictions.

This house, for instance. So big. So old and rambling, yet surprisingly modern and comfortable notwithstanding.

And that man—the man Riddley Fenton. A contradiction, too. Shabby and dusty and work-stained and tough. Also suavely polite, pleasantly witty when he wasn't being scathing, unexpectedly sophisticated, patently widely informed.

And domineering.

Emmie supposed it was that last quality in him that made her take a deep, steadying, purposeful breath as she pushed open the dining-room door and entered.

As it happened, the breath was wasted, unnecessary, since the only other person in the room this morning wasn't Riddley Fenton at all.

Emmie expelled her breath again and smiled shyly at the fair-headed young man who was sitting there, busily tucking into an enormous plateful of steak and eggs.

'Good morning.'

'Oh! Hullo.' The chair scraped back as he stood up and grinned at her, put out a hand. 'Miss Montfort, isn't it? Ridd said I was to look out for you, and see that you ate a decent breakfast. He says you could do with feeding up.'

'Does he?' She made a face. 'That makes me sound like one of his precious animals, bound for slaughter. Do sit down again and carry on.'

She took the chair opposite, helped herself to orange juice from the frosted jug in the centre of the table. The young man went on eating his steak and eggs with his former relish, apparently quite unabashed that he now had company. Emmie, studying him, saw that he was actually older than she had thought at first. He must be about her own age,

51

she decided. Certainly not the callow youth she had first taken him for. There was the firmness of maturity about his shaven chin, a certain quiet assurance about his person and his movements that only experience can put there. A likeable young man, she reflected. The steady, dependable sort. She wondered who he could be, and what he was doing here, eating such a hearty breakfast at Riddley Fenton's own dining-table.

As if in answer to her unspoken speculation, he looked up and smiled again, with an engagingly open friendliness.

'Condor's my name, Miss Montfort, Kevin Condor. Book-keeper extraordinary, and Ridd's right-hand man as well. You'd better call me Kev, since everyone does out here.'

'Then you must call me Emmie,' she returned warmly, responding to his friendly approach with eagerness. What a relief to find someone in this place who was actually *disposed* to be pleasant, after that Fenton man and his bossiness!

'Emmie—that's right. Ridd told me that too.' He pushed his empty plate to one side, helped himself to toast, and reached for the marmalade. 'Pity you came out here all that way for nothing, Emmie. I'm really sorry, because I can just imagine how disappointed you must be. Ridd's pretty mad himself, actually—what with the lawyers down there not putting you wise at the start, like he instructed them to. There seems to have been a slip-up somewhere.'

A slip-up! That was putting it mildly, thought Emmie grimly. She had burned her boats, severed her connections, abandoned her now-resentful brothers and sisters, thrown up her *all*, to come, and he called it a slip-up! She gulped miserably, tried to smile.

'Never mind,' Kevin told her kindly. 'Ridd'll put you on the nine-fifty on Thursday, and you'll be able to forget it ever happened. Right now, you might as well make up your mind to enjoy your couple of days with us, beginning this minute. Help yourself to eggs and some steak. On that covered hot-plate on the sideboard.'

'No, thanks.'

'Go on, Emmie. Please. Ridd'll give me hell if you don't.'

'Where *is*—er—Ridd?'

She must speak to him! He'd promised, hadn't he? Promised that he'd sort things out this morning. He wasn't going to pack her off on the train again, as he thought, so the sooner they had this discussion the better.

'He's out.'

'*Out?*'

'Well, of course. He's out cutting scrub for the ewes on the Bradley's Plains block, the same as he was yesterday. Rode out at piccaninny daylight.'

So there *had* been sounds in that pre-dawn hush, after all! The muffled sounds of elastic-sided boots on the veranda boards outside her room! The faintest squeak of the hinged gauze door as Riddley Fenton let himself out of his house and crossed the lawn in the direction of the yards. He'd gone without even speaking to her, without waiting to see her this morning. He didn't even intend that there should *be* a discussion.

'Ridd was thinking Miss Millicent's beneficiary would be an older person,' Kevin was saying now, conversationally. 'I mean, we all did, naturally.'

'Did you know Millie, Kev? Miss Millicent, I mean?'

'Yes, we all did,' he said again. 'I mean, we got all our stores there, y'see. She took it over from the Bradys, and we kept on going for our supplies. Everything from a crochet-hook to a tin of dip, she stocked, the same as the Bradys did before her. She was a quaint old dear, eccentric, but we all liked her, and the kids themselves doted on her. For an elderly spinster she certainly had a way with children. I reckon that's what settled her to staying in the first place, the chance of being a mother to those three kids from the Far-out Homes. She said the district wasn't what she'd been looking for exactly, but I think the kids won her over to retiring here.'

'She'd been used to children all her life.' Emmie nodded to herself, her eyes suddenly misty as she recalled Millie's great

53

kindness, her sense of fun, her justice, her extraordinary understanding of the very young. 'Kevin, where *are* those children?'

He wiped his lips, slipped his napkin into its wooden ring and laid it to one side, standing up.

'The kids? Susan Wensley has them at the moment.'

'Who is Susan Wensley?'

'The schoolteacher at Koolonga. Just over the rise from the store, as a matter of fact. Look, Emmie, if you'll excuse me, I'm afraid I'll have to be off.'

'Is she old, this Susan Wensley? Like Miss Millicent?'

'Susan? Good lord, no! Anything but!'

Something in the way he spoke, an odd inflection, together with the faint wave of colour that crept up beneath his tan, made Kevin Condor look suddenly self-conscious and a whole five years younger at the same time. Instinct told Emmie, always sensitive to the feelings of others, that the topic of Susan Wensley was not a welcome one at that moment. Her intuition was reinforced by the manner in which her companion grabbed his hat, and with a muttered 'See you at lunch,' disappeared hurriedly out the door.

Moments later she heard him whistling as he went down the path. Whatever had upset him, Kevin Condor hadn't been long in recovering his equilibrium. Or was that jaunty whistling a pose? She hoped she had not unwittingly offended him in some way, because he was a likeable man, and could perhaps prove a useful ally. Emmie had a feeling that she was going to need all the allies she could muster!

With a sigh, she went back to her room, tidied her few unpacked possessions, and then walked in the direction of the kitchen.

It occupied a separate block, reached by a narrow, covered path of cement. Basketed geraniums hung on either side, and a grapevine wove pale tendrils amongst the wires that enclosed the path. It was leafy, cool, enclosed. Even that utilitarian corridor possessed the same rambling attraction as the shaded lawns, dappled arbours and shrouded shrubberies that abounded beyond the gauzed verandas of the house itself.

Mrs. Bexley was folding sheets at a long wooden table. When Emmie offered to help she was handed a pair of folded ends without demur. The housekeeper was that sort of person- forthright, capable, with a strong-featured face, and a natural dignity which Emmie immediately appreciated. She felt that here was a person who would be unquestionably loyal, without pretence or deviousness, and she supposed that it was for these qualities, as well as for sheer capability, that Riddley Fenton must have chosen this woman to run his straggling and complicated homestead for him.

'Can you manage with that hand?' Mrs. Bexley smiled. 'I think you're better today, Miss Montfort. Ridd was quite concerned about you last night. Said you looked as if you'd blow away as easy as a piece of thistledown.'

'I'm a lot sturdier than I look, I can assure you,' Emmie told her quickly, adding a little grimly, 'And I don't blow away too easily, either. Nor do I intend to be *sent* away, Mrs. Bexley, and that's what I came to see you about just now. I don't want to go on that train on Thursday, so there are a few things I'll need to know, you see.'

'I'm not sure that I *do* see.' The older woman gave her a direct look. 'That, surely, is a matter between yourself and Ridd, my dear? It's up to Ridd entirely what he chooses to do. He's the boss here, you know.'

'But not *my* boss.'

'Ridd knows what's best. Whatever he decides, I'm sure it'll be the right thing. And, as I said, it's nothing whatever to do with me, and knowing him as I do I wouldn't dare to question whatever line he takes. Neither is it my place to do so, you must see that.'

Mrs. Bexley's lips were now firmly pursed, and there was an adamant glint in her eye as she brought her hands together over the sheet-ends which Emmie was holding, and took them from her.

'I'm—I'm not suggesting that you actually *do* anything,' Emmie defended herself miserably. 'I just want to ask a few questions, that's all.'

'Ask away, then,' was the brisk retort. 'But if you expect me to go behind Ridd's back in any way, you'll have to think again, Miss Montfort. I'm sorry, but that's the way it is. He's the best employer *I've* ever had, and I'm not alone in saying that. Every single person on this station would tell you the same thing—and beyond it as well. And what he says goes. One doesn't argue with Ridd Fenton—not if one has any sense at *all*.'

Emmie swallowed.

'You know why I came here, Mrs. Bexley?'

'It seems you came to claim that store, the one at the siding that Miss Millicent had. Funny, I got to know Miss Millicent quite well, but never once did she even mention you. It was only when the will turned up that any of us heard your name for the first time, so you can hardly blame Ridd for being a bit bowled over when he found you there in the shop last night—just a slip of a kid, he said, and a city one at that, and looking as lost as a kitten in a woodpile.'

'Yes—well, never mind that just now.' Emmie shifted her position uncomfortably. She didn't specially *want* to hear what Riddley Fenton's exact words had been! 'All I need, Mrs. Bexley, is just to *know* a few things. It's not very easy, coming to a completely new district.' She paused, smiled appeasingly. 'You can guess how different it is from the city, can't you? I just wondered about the people, the general layout, I mean—if they *had* been going to be my neighbours,' she hastened to emphasise, and was rewarded at last to see a more co-operative light appear in the other's wrinkled face.

'What, for instance'—Emmie pursued her advantage—'happened to those three children when Millie went? I thought perhaps they'd have been sent back to the Homes where they came from?'

'No, Ridd wanted to avoid that if he possibly could. He'd

have taken them here himself permanently, rather than risk them being split up again at the Orphanage. Not that children aren't well cared for there, you understand, but having been in a private home they'd got a taste of being together in a family unit, so to speak, and there'd have been a distinct likelihood of their being sent out again to different places if they'd gone back. We did have them here for a couple of nights, as a matter of fact, and then Susan offered to have them.'

'Susan Wensley?'

'That's right. It's worked out quite well so far. She's a very capable girl, is Susan—enormously so, in fact—and there's plenty of room in the house that goes along with her job as schoolteacher. Their education is automatically taken care of, too. That's another thing that was important to Ridd.'

'Doesn't she mind being—er—saddled with three children, when she's already got her teaching to cope with as well?'

Mrs. Bexley gave Emmie an odd look.

'Not that you'd notice. Susan would do anything for Ridd —and why should she mind, when the "something" she's doing in this case brings him over to see her? He goes over now far more often than ever before. *She* won't complain, not even about a parcel of children, if they bring him a bit nearer. And I don't suppose he will, either.'

'He—he goes to see the children?'

'He goes to see them *all*.' Mrs. Bexley put away the last sheet with an air of finality. 'There's plenty of speculation about who he likes to see *best* once he gets there, though ! But that's not for me to repeat, so I'd be grateful if you wouldn't, either. Ridd has made himself responsible for these children, and he'll see the thing through in whatever way he has to. So will Susan. She's a fine girl, that, and she's been through a sad time. I don't suppose either of them was actually *wanting* to be landed with Miss Millicent's foster-children, but they're in kind hands, I can assure you. You needn't give them another thought.'

But Emmie *was* giving them another thought. She was thinking very hard indeed, right then.

'Used Mr.—er—Fenton go over to visit Susan before the children went there?' she asked now, idly.

'Well, yes, sometimes he did. As I said, Susan's had a bad time, and naturally Ridd was counted upon to help her in whatever way he could. He's always helping folk, that man. You've no idea the number of people who come to him for advice of one sort and another, from all over the west.'

And I bet he just *loves* giving it, thought Emmie sourly to herself. How that man revelled in being the king-pin, the boss-cocky of the whole area! You could see it a mile off!

And now he thought he was going to boss her, too, in the same way as he did those others. But if he expected that she was going to be just as grateful and submissive and obedient as the rest, then Mr. Riddley Fenton was in for something of a shock.

Thistledown, indeed!

Emmie wandered around the garden for a while, lost in thought. Her surroundings bathed her in a green, soothing tranquillity that enabled her to assemble her ideas. Indeed, the gardens, watered by the piped taps and hoses that were supplied from the adjacent bore, were the only green and growing things in the way of vegetation around here. Outside the homestead fence, everything was brown and beaten and dry. Inside, it was like a bright oasis.

It was the heat of that fierce sun beating down upon her bare head that finally drove her indoors again, and when lunchtime came it was a relief to find that the meal was an entirely cold one—a simple salad to accompany the thin slices of corned silverside, and an interesting selection of cheeses displayed on a polished wooden board with an assortment of biscuits and a dish of butter-pats.

Emmie must have shown her surprise at the varied array, for Kevin grinned and explained with a certain satisfied pride that there was always a decent choice of cheeses at Koolonga homestead because they were something for which the boss happened to cherish a particular fondness.

'The boss? You mean—er—Ridd?'

'Who else?'

Emmie was thinking automatically of that store again. She hadn't naturally, had time to check the muddle of dust-laden stock, and of course there'd be no perishables left over after this long interval, but if she were going to supply the homestead it might be diplomatic to discover what the owner liked. Choice, and quality, he had told her, were better at Berroola Junction. She must see to it that he could not validly make such a comment once *she* took over.

'Where, in Berroola, do you get cheeses like that?' she asked.

'Stone the flipping crows, girl! They're not from Berroola, *those* ones!' Kev seemed amused at her naïve assumption. 'Those are from the city. The Big Smoke.'

'Does he order them, to come up on the train?'

'No, he doesn't order them. He chooses them himself when he's down. Ridd's often there on business, you see. And he doesn't go by train when he does go, either. It'd take much too long.'

'How, then?'

'The same way as he goes almost everywhere, Emmie. By plane.'

'His *own* plane?'

'Well, of course—one of his company's, anyway. He's got a lot of country to keep an eye on, you know. Different properties, in widely scattered areas. The plane's the thing these days, when time is so precious. It's an easy way to collect one's cheese, too.'

Now he was teasing her!

Emmie flushed, pink at her own sheer ignorance. She was pondering her chances of bluffing her way into what she intended to do. Perhaps she could actually turn her own innocence to good account. One never suspects the innocent of being unscrupulously scheming!

'I've a lot to learn,' she heard herself admitting with convincing humility. 'And the sooner I start, the better, I should think, Kevin. Could you take me back to the store now, please, if it's convenient?'

'Back? But I thought you were staying here. That's what Ridd gave me to understand.'

'*Did* he? No, surely not. You must have mistaken what he meant. We sorted it all out last night, you see. I'll just get my things together, if it wouldn't be a bother.'

'No bother. It's just——' The young man scratched his head in perplexity. 'I was *sure* Ridd said that you were staying here and going back on the train on Thursday.'

'No, you've got it wrong, truly. I told him yesterday what my intentions were.' She managed a well-feigned surprise. Well, it was true, that bit, wasn't it, anyway? She *had* told him what her intentions were. It wasn't her fault if he had refused to believe her, or to agree.

She really didn't need his agreement, either. There was a lot to be said for a *fait accompli*. Present him with that, and there'd be no further point in discussing the matter. Emmie suspected that 'discussions' with a man like Ridd Fenton could prove to be curiously one-sided affairs, best avoided if one could manage it.

It was less difficult than she had anticipated, that getaway from the Koolonga homestead.

On the final assumption that the master of the house had already known and approved, Kevin Condor set himself out to be as helpful as possible. He not only carried her luggage from the bedroom to the long, shining Chevrolet—Ridd Fenton's, no less!—that was now waiting at the front steps, but he also brought her some eggs and a side of bacon from the kitchen block, and a basket of freshly picked tomatoes from the garden.

'Take some of that cheese too,' he offered, with somewhat reckless generosity.

'Oh no, I *couldn't* do that!' Emmie was aghast. Her conscience was giving her a few painful twinges at accepting this other bounty, in any case, and now, as she recalled

60

precisely whose cheeses they were, it tugged her afresh. Bad enough that he should find *her* gone, but—his cheeses as well? Oh no!

'No cheese,' she said firmly. 'But I'm very grateful for the rest, if it can be spared. I'll pay it back, of course,' she assured Kevin gravely.

'Good heavens, you don't need to do that—not out in these parts, Emmie. You can look on that little bit of tucker as buckshee. A traveller's rights, no strings attached. Why, even a swagman gets his hand-out if he calls, although it's tea and sugar and flour he'll settle for, more than likely. So why shouldn't you?'

Emmie could have replied that a swagman wasn't usually employed in intentionally deceiving the station boss, like she was, but she somehow refrained. Instead she climbed into the saloon, settled herself back comfortably in the spacious interior, and they were off.

It was warm in the car, even with the window open. The tyres threw up a wake of dust when they left the shaded seclusion of the tree-lined avenue and sped over the ramp and on to the open track. The country shimmered in a blue haze of heat. Now she could see the dearth of green, the dryness of the desiccated landscape, the arid creek-beds, stony and bare, the wilted matt of yellowing vegetation that in the jeep's headlights last night she had assumed to be lush with life. No feeding there, he had said, and Ridd Fenton had certainly been right!

The memory of his grim, preoccupied profile as he had spoken those words caused Emmie a small pang of contrition, almost of pure guilt. How tired he had looked! How dusty and begrimed! Weary in mind and sinewy limb. Depressed, no doubt, by the sight of his weakened stock and the lack of feed for his starving animals. It couldn't be a pleasant occupation, wielding an axe all day in this dust and heat, lopping down branches for those pathetic, scraggy, dying creatures, while the crows wheeled nearer, nearer, waiting, waiting, for the moment when yet another animal would give up the struggle and succumb, a bloated brown carcase on the bare brown plain.

Well, in a way, she was doing Riddley Fenton a favour by leaving just now, wasn't she? At least she wasn't *adding* to his problems, but subtracting one of them by her own removal. Just as soon as she got that store-cum-dwelling place scrubbed out and in order, she would take the children back, and that would be another thing off the man's mind, too. Yes, she was actually doing Ridd Fenton a turn, asserting her independence like this. She'd make a happy home for those children once again, too. Not that they weren't being looked after, but it would be nice for them to be able to leave the little school each afternoon, like all the others, wouldn't it? Nicer than just going back inside the schoolhouse again. There wasn't much variety about that! Much better to come running back over the rise and along the rutted road to Millie's little store, where Emmie would have nice things waiting for their tea—freshly baked delicious-smelling things that Susan Wensley couldn't possibly be expected to have ready, not when she was teaching all day herself as well.

The thought of her little 'family' depending upon her was a strangely cheering one just then, when Emmie knew that she was presently to be confronted with the bleakness and isolation of Miss Millicent's General Store again. As soon as she got there she would start to transform the bleakness into cleanliness and comfort, though. And by the time Riddley Fenton saw it again he would also see that she was neither weak *nor* helpless, and that she meant just what she said. She meant business! He was bound to be impressed by the transformation she intended to bring about, wasn't he, and it would be more difficult for him to sustain his arguments in the face of the positive action she was about to take.

'It's good of you to bring me, Kevin. I hope I haven't taken you away from something important?'

'Nothing that won't keep, Emmie.'

'Maybe you could just let Susan Wensley know that I'll be coming for those kids in a couple of days, while you're out in the car, and so near?'

Kevin glanced at his watch, hesitated.

'I think I'll leave that to Ridd, if you don't mind.'

Something in his tone made her look his way curiously.

'Don't you *like* Susan Wensley, Kev?' she asked, reluctant to give way to her inquisitiveness, but somehow unable to help the question.

'Susan's a very nice girl.' His tone was now carefully flat.

A very nice girl. Well, that seemed to make *two* people who thought that particular thing about that particular young woman. The two being Kevin Condor, who had just said as much, and Riddley Fenton himself.

'Have you been about here long, Kevin? In the Koolonga district?'

'Not always, no. I was brought up in Victoria, actually. I'm a Gippslander, Emmie. But I jackerooed up here for two years after I left school. Then I got called up. Training, then war service. You know the routine. After which I came back.'

Emmie nodded soberly. Suddenly she knew the reason for that old-young look about Kevin which had puzzled her from the start, and which never quite left his face. He had had to become a man at a time when he was still in all essentials a mere boy, and now he could never recapture the cleancut youthful zest that should have been his. You couldn't turn the clock back upon experience, even Emmie knew that.

'It was while I was away that Sue got married,' Kevin volunteered suddenly, in a bleak voice. 'I often feel that if I hadn't had to go just when I did——'

He broke off, manoeuvred the car around a stump with easy skill and smiled apologetically, as if ashamed at this indiscretion.

'Mind if I smoke?'

'Not at all. Go ahead. I didn't realise Susan *is* married,' Emmie observed after a small silence.

'Not is. Was. Sue is a widow, Emmie. She lost her chap in

a car crash, just a few months after their wedding. It was one of those tempestuous affairs, meeting one week, marrying almost the next—you know the sort of thing. Not like Sue at all, actually. I heard the news when I was away.' His voice was expressionless. 'And then it hardly seemed any time at all after I heard the first lot of news that the second lot arrived.' A brittle laugh. 'Odd to be confronted with that sort of thing when you're away on a survival course, training in every conceivable method of self-defence, every artifice for self-preservation that the book can throw at you, all designed with the specific purpose of helping you to stay alive. And then you hear that a cove's been killed, just alone in his utility, with nobody gunning for him at all, and just because the heat builds up and bursts his tyre at the wrong moment on the wrong corner. It makes you reckon you've got a sporting chance after all.'

'It must have been awful.'

A feeble observation, but Emmie felt she had to say something. She wished she could think of something less ineffectual than what she had just said, something that would wipe away the bitterness from Kevin Condor's nice blue eyes, erase those ageing lines of memory from his young–old face.

There was nothing that she could possibly add that wouldn't sound even more fatuous.

She looked away. A stand of ring-barked timber lay to the left, a gaunt ghost-scrub, as gaunt and bleak as her companion's expression. Among the bleached trunks scrambled dry grasses and reeds, and a few taller rushes with nodding black heads that looked like guardsmen's busbies. A lizard rustled through the undergrowth and climbed along one of the fallen branches, lay inert as the car passed close, beady eyes staring, collar frilled in alarm. Its gaping yellow throat was as golden as a mustard-flower against the bark-like drabness of the grey head.

'I guess at first, when I heard that Sue had hardly waited to get me out of the way before she up and married this other bloke—well, I thought, what the hell, I wouldn't care if I collected one for keeps. But you *do*, you know. The instinct for survival is stronger than you think. And then, when I heard what had happened to Sue, my only wish was to get back to Koolonga Station as quickly as I possibly could, back to her. Death was something to be avoided at all costs, because Sue was alone, and it would have prevented me from getting back to help her. My philosophy altered from the passive conviction to the positive one.'

> *'Thou hast not lived, why shouldst thou perish so?*
> *Thou hadst* one *aim*, one *business*, one *desire.'*

Kevin glanced at her appreciatively as Emmie quoted the lines in a softly thoughtful voice.

'Exactly, Emmie.' A deprecating shrug. 'Look here, I don't know why I'm telling you all this. It must be that understanding, gentle little face of yours. It doesn't judge one.'

'I haven't enough experience to presume to judge,' she replied frankly.

And judging one's fellow mortals *was* a presumption, that was certain. Emmie put aside the fleeting vision of Riddley Fenton's swiftly disapproving scowl, and returned her eyes to the monotony of the brown, bare plain.

Finally she looked back at the young man who was guiding the big Chev saloon over the corrugated track.

'Well, having told me so much, you might as well finish,' she prompted gently. 'You came home, and——?'

'And nothing, really.' He shrugged again, but Emmie thought she detected a depth of hurt beneath the simulated carelessness. Yes, she was sure that she had not been deceived. 'I suppose Sue had changed. One would, naturally, after what she'd been through, and I couldn't get back before my time was up and I was demobbed. There were no compassionate grounds on which to return. I mean, hang it all, she hadn't even been my fiancée. Perhaps it had all been too long, that interval. At any rate, she was withdrawn and ill at ease with me from the very start. She didn't seem to need me as I'd hoped and dreamed she might. I can't reach her now.'

'Have you tried?'

'Up to a point.' He sounded suddenly terse. 'I'm not going to prostrate myself on the ground, though, if that's what she's waiting for. She seems keener on accepting other people's help than mine, so I reckon I'm not going to push it. She's changed. She's hard, self-sufficient, quite different.'

Emmie was silent about that. What, after all, could she say that would be of any comfort? It was obvious to her what had happened. In Kevin's unavoidable absence, other people had been on the spot when Susan Wensley had needed that help most. They had been available, where Kevin had not been, at a time when Susan had been at her most vulnerable. People like Riddley Fenton himself, for instance. The domineering, managing sort, who liked nothing better than to dole out advice to helpless women. And what sort of a chance, when he came home, would a sensitive, retiring, idealistic boy like Kevin Condor have against a hard-bitten, worldly type like the boss of Koolonga Station?

Their minds had apparently gravitated in the same direction.

'Ridd's been good to Sue. Good to me, too, since I came home,' Kevin stated now, gruffly. 'I finished my jackerooing, and then took a book-keeping course by correspondence, and he offered me the job I have now—a sort of roving commission. Some days I'm out on the run, others I'm in the office. I can turn my hand to most things on the property, and I'm never bored. It's a job in a million, and Ridd's a generous employer, the best a chap could ask for.'

How could Kevin bear to be so charitable about the man who had supplanted him in Sue Wensley's affections?

Poor Kevin! Emmie could see, clearly enough, how he was placed. The man who had kept his place open for him while he was away in that ghastly Vietnam was also the man

66

who had come between himself and Susan. He could not find it in his heart to blame Ridd, though, and so the entire force of his bitterness was directed against Susan herself.

No wonder he spoke in that terse, bitter way! No wonder his approach to her was so cautious. No, not cautious. *Hopeless*.

Emmie sat back against the luxurious leather upholstery and seethed.

How callous, how insensitive that Fenton man was, not to see what an invidious position this poor young employee was in, and through no fault of his own. All because he had gone off to fight for his country—or for that dim, unreal cause that was supposed to be synonymous with patriotism!—he hadn't been *there*, and Riddley Fenton *had*. Surely, even if the Fenton man were serious over this girl, the decent, gentlemanly thing to do would have been to stand aside and let Kevin have his chance? After all, it was Kevin who had been courting her before he went away. By all accounts Riddley Fenton had had no interest in her *then*!

He wasn't a gentleman, that was clear. And what was more, decided Emmie hotly to herself, he probably *enjoyed* cutting out the opposition in that ruthless, remorseless way of his. He probably got a real kick out of the situation! Well, the less she saw of him personally, the better. Once she got those children safely over here, there shouldn't be any need to have much to do with him at all.

'Here we are, then.' Kevin interrupted her churning thoughts.

In the harsh, early afternoon light, the store appeared even more derelict than she had remembered. The dust gave the counters and tumbled stock a powdery sort of unreality, as though she had stepped into a veritable ghost-town. Chains of cobweb festooned the ceiling, strung sagging, beady threads from chair to shelf, from window to floor. The very undisturbedness was in itself disturbing. Eerie.

Nowhere, at the back of nowhere. Beyond even the *beyond*.

Once Kevin left her, the only other living things besides herself would be those spiders, and at the moment even they were inactive. Or perhaps they had left, too. Perhaps it had been too lonely even for them!

Behind her, Kevin cleared his throat.

'Sure you'll be all right?'

'Of course.' There was far more confidence in her smile than she was actually feeling.

'Well——' He hesitated, put out an awkward hand. 'I'll see you, Emmie.'

'Yes, see you.' She smiled again, bravely, and shook hands, since that seemed to be what he expected.

To Emmie it savoured of finality, that handshake.

She watched from the front veranda until Kevin's big, dust-covered car (or rather, Riddley Fenton's big, dust-covered car!) had disappeared, right into a distant clump of mulga, and then she walked slowly back inside.

Into her own place. Her very own inheritance.

Emmie squared her slim shoulders, and resolution took control.

The first thing Emmie did, that afternoon, was to gather some wood from the surrounding scrub and light the large old-fashioned cooking range. She dragged logs and branches patiently, choosing the smaller ones which she knew she could handle, and stacking them carefully in a pile in one of the sheds at the back of the premises.

She worked under the blazing sun, with the shantung-baku hat perched on her small brown head, pulling and tugging at the wretched things until her face was scarlet, and the bandage on her left hand filthy with grime. When she had got a good supply, she chopped enough for her present needs, breaking the thinner pieces with the back of the heavy axe which she had found, and cutting stubbornly into the thicker ones with biting strokes that seldom landed in the same place twice, until they yielded. She might not be much of a wood-chopper, but Emmie had no intention of doing battle with that treacherous little kerosene cooker again. She would need some shorter pieces of wood, too, to feed that mysterious-looking chip heater in the bathroom. The thought of a soak in warm soapy water, when all her chores were accomplished, was enough to set Emmie swinging the axe with fresh determination.

When the water was hot, she commenced her scrubbing programme.

All the moveable furniture had to be got out on to the veranda, and then she had to dust down the entire interior before she could wash down the walls and floor.

Emmie worked at speed, swiped down the spiders' webs with almost hysterical fervour, trying not to think about those fat, scuttling, venom-filled bodies as she chased them frantically as they fell and clobbered them with the back of her long-handled broom.

Instead, she thought about her family, and with a certain grim amusement. If they could see her now!

Emmie could just imagine Sharon's fastidious gestures of distaste, Lissa's condescending pity, Robert's unnerving compassion, and Mark's demoralising sneer—the one that said I-told-you-so as clearly as if he had spoken the words aloud.

The light was fading by the time she turned out the two adjoining bedrooms and scrubbed them, too, but this time she was better prepared. She had trimmed the wicks and filled the lamps, and now she lit them carefully and placed them in strategically chosen positions, to give her the best possible illumination.

A pity she had no idea how to start the electricity generator in the little power-house out there. Since the place was wired and fitted with a civilised lighting system, that must be the obvious purpose of the small green engine embedded in its concrete floor. One glance at a complicated switchboard and rows of glass batteries had been enough to tell her that she'd be out of her depth in even trying to get the thing started, though. A burnt hand was bad enough. She'd be of no use to those children if she went and got herself electrocuted.

Emmie restoked the chip heater. Once the water became hot again after all she'd drawn off for scrubbing, she'd have that longed-for bath.

In the meantime, hunger was the most demanding contingency.

She had just found the frying pan, and was about to cut some slices from the side of bacon which Kevin had given her, when she heard the car coming round to the back of the store.

No, not a car. Ridd Fenton's jeep. Emmie drew the pan to one side, put the bacon back into its wrapping and waited for him to come in.

It was something of an anticlimax when he did not come in at all! She waited a while longer, tense and expectant, her heart beating almost in her very throat as she mentally steeled herself for battle. Finally, when he still didn't come, she opened the back door and peeped out. Immediately the torch which had been playing over the pile of fresh-cut logs detached itself from that target and pinned her in its beam.

'Tired of my hospitality already, it seems, Miss Montfort.'

Riddley Fenton's harsh tone, leaping out of the darkness, was even chillier than she had anticipated. It was deep and emphatic, with the careful coldness of controlled anger. As he stepped into the light from her own doorway and flicked off the torch, Emmie could see that his face was set in hard, unyielding lines, his eyes stormy and dark and accusing.

With a grip that bit into her soft flesh, he took her arm and turned her abruptly indoors again.

'Come here. I want a *word* with you,' he announced grimly, and to Emmie, wincing at his hold and shivering with sudden apprehension, it seemed that she'd be lucky indeed if a *word* was all she got off with!

CHAPTER FOUR

THE whole place still reeked of damp wood and carbolic.

Emmie saw Ridd Fenton wrinkle his nose and cast a quick, comprehensive glance around him. Pride spurted in her at the transformation she had wrought, but if he noticed any improvement he certainly wasn't going to applaud it. By the look of things, he wasn't in an applauding sort of mood.

'Just what do you think you're playing at, Miss Montfort, jumping the gun like this? I suppose you told Kev a whole pack of lies in order to skin out like that while I was off. Did you reckon that by moving in and staking a claim you'd have a stronger case for staying?'

His supposition was so nearly accurate that Emmie caught her breath.

'You said you'd discuss it today,' she returned woodenly. 'You promised. And you *didn't*.'

'So what? It's still today, isn't it?' He had removed his wide-brimmed hat and thrown it on a table—a table which Emmie was pleased to see now shone darkly clean, free from its former pallid coating of dust. Again Riddley Fenton didn't seem to notice. He didn't even look around him any more. He just ran his fingers through his black hair where it had been flattened by the hat, and confronted her with a steely grey gaze. 'You were sleeping when I left this morning. Oh, yes, you were,' he emphasised, as she opened her mouth to deny it. 'I looked in on my way out, and you were dead to the world. You looked as innocent as a babe, I might tell you, lying there on those pillows, but we both know you're not that, don't we, you underhand little schemer.'

'Now look here, Mr. Fenton, you'd promised, and when I heard you'd gone I just thought——'

'You can call me Ridd,' he interrupted her brusquely. 'Everyone calls me that. It doesn't *mean* anything, so don't go all wide-eyed at the invitation.'

'Emily, then,' she replied feebly, scarlet, reluctant.

'Well, you listen to me, Emily, will you? If you think a busy man like myself is going to hang around the homestead while my sheep are starving until *you* happen to choose to open those big, wide, innocent eyes of yours just so we can discuss a relatively unimportant matter of no comparative urgency——'

'Urgent to *me*. Important to *me*,' she broke in huskily. Oh, if only he could know *how* important!

Something in her expression caused his eyes to narrow, making her wriggle uncomfortably.

'Yes, that's what I mean,' he said thoughtfully. 'Just why, I ask myself, should a broken-down shack in the back of beyond attain that sort of importance to anyone? What's behind it? Why have you come here, Miss—Emily? Are you running away from something?'

'That's my affair.'

She managed a quiet dignity, but she couldn't meet those keen, glittery eyes, for all that. What if she admitted it? What if she'd said yes, my family, *that's* what I'm running away from? My brilliant, oppressive, possessive, stultifying family, whom you know and admire along with all the rest of the world. He'd sell her out, wouldn't he, if he knew? He'd regard it as his bounden duty, of course, to return the straying black sheep to the comfortable, cloying, unadventurous fold, where she was never allowed to emerge as a real person.

'It must be something big to send you haring out here with that look of desperation. What is it? A man?'

'It's my business, as I've already said.' She shrugged, for all she found herself completely startled at the sheer impossibility. The shy, obscure little Emmie Montfort never tangled

72

with *men*, but he needn't know that, need he? She didn't deny it, and he could now assume what he liked. It had been his idea, after all, not hers, and she hadn't even had to lie. Better that he should think a man was the reason than that he should suspect her connection with those other Montforts, whom he had known and liked from past associations.

'You've made it my business too.' He was summing her up again with that long, speculative look. 'It must have been one hell of a shattering affair, emotionally I mean, to make you drop everything and run out on him like this. Are you sure you know what you're doing?'

'*Positive!* Now look, Mr. Fenton——'

'Ridd.'

'Ridd. I'm tired. As you can see, if you'd only bother to look around you, I've had a busy afternoon. I've chopped wood, too, as well as all this dusting and scrubbing. I'm also hungry, and dirty. I need a bath, and——'

'And we're going to thrash out this affair. If you think you'll talk more sense clean—well, go and get spruced up. That bandage is dirty, by the way. I'll put a clean one on for you after your bath. I've a kit in the jeep.'

She was taken aback.

'I'm—I'm asking you to *go*.'

'And I've said I'll wait,' he retorted tersely. 'If you don't go and get in that tub, I'll take you there and put you in myself. Now, get going, Emily.'

Emily did. In some haste. She could see that it wasn't safe to argue a moment longer. You didn't dawdle when the Ridd Fentons of this world said to 'get going' in that particular kind of voice. You didn't wait to see if they meant it, because something told you that that wasn't safe, either!

Emmie pulled a quilted housecoat out of her case, grabbed her satin mules from the corner where she had stuffed them to save space and departed.

When she came back, she was fresh and clean and in a humbler frame of mind. Her hair clung damply to her nape and her skin felt pleasantly smooth and fragrant under a liberal dusting of the expensive powder which Lissa had given her last Christmas. There had been an enormous drum of the stuff, with its own large, splendid swansdown puff which was inclined to disperse its burden everywhere but on target. The air in the bathroom was thick with it this minute, and there were several white blotches of it at the base of Emmie's throat, plus a dab near her ear which she hadn't bothered to remove, just in case the man thought she was being—well, 'Eve'-ish. Seductive, if you like. It was hardly proper, finding oneself alone with a man in this outlandish place at this hour, but you could hardly be accused of seductiveness if you'd blobbed your powder on in careless blotches, and left your hair in tiny unkempt tendrils without even bothering to run a comb through it. And her nose was terribly sunburnt on the tip, too. It would probably peel later, because the shantung baku hat wasn't intended for a country sunstopper, at all.

The intermingling smell of Lissa's powder and the carbolic which had hitherto predominated was an oddly reassuring mixture to Emmie just then. Much more reassuring than the keen look she received from the dark, unfathomable man who was waiting for her in one of Millie's shabby chairs.

For the second time she was forced to allow him to deal with her hand.

'You'd better sit this time,' he instructed, in a clipped, impersonal way, and Emmie did so.

When he had finished, he resumed his own chair and looked at her squarely.

'I'll see it again in a day or two. Just see that you keep it covered and clean. That's if you're still *here* in a day or two,' he added as an afterthought.

Emmie flushed. 'What makes you think I won't be?'

'What makes you think you *will* be?'

'I'm my own mistress, aren't I?' she replied with deceptive meekness. 'I've told you already, I intend to make my home here. And a home for those children too, of course.'

'Aha!' He pounced. 'And now we're coming to the point.'

'What point?'

'How can I be sure that you'll be a suitable guardian for those children?'

'You can't be sure, but *I* know that I can be, and *you* will just have to take me on trust.' She pushed her damp hair back wearily. 'Don't you ever take anyone on trust, Mr. Fenton?'

'Ridd.'

'Don't you, Ridd? Not ever?'

'Yes, sometimes I do, when the evidence points to it being warranted. In this instance——' His doubt hung in the air, a fraught silence between them.

'You aren't sure.' She finished the sentence for him.

'That's right, I'm not sure.'

'No one can be sure of anything in this life. No one can be sure of tomorrow, sure that the sun will even rise. No one can be sure that there's even a God. You've got to take some things on trust.' Emmie found herself warming to her theme.

Sadly, he wasn't impressed.

'Some things, I agree. But we happen to be discussing things temporal, not things spiritual,' he pointed out dryly. 'It's easier to pin down the material possibilities.' Relentlessly, he began to do some of that pinning down. 'Have you, for instance, any previous experience with children?'

'Oh, heaps and heaps,' she assured him airily.

And *what* experience!

She pushed aside the mental vision of Lorna's tiny fist clutching a defiant handful of best blue ostrich feathers from her best blue hat while she worked on, unaided, at those wretched piles of sandwiches, thrust away the memory of her calculated smack on her niece's white-frilled bottom, and the resulting defiant gesture that had brought all Lorna's raspberry squash down over her delightful white organdie party-dress.

'*Lots* of experience,' she repeated, in heartfelt tones.

'I see.' His mouth twitched, and there was a betraying glint in his eye. 'A *wealth* of experience with children,' he murmured, 'though hardly more than a child herself. Right, then, that's that point taken care of. Now for the next. Presumably you'll have some form of transport, to get you and them about?'

Emmie stared blankly. She should have thought of that, but somehow she hadn't. The need for a car had never occurred to her, because she had imagined that she'd be in the middle of a small country town, a close-knit community, where the bell on Millie's little shop door would be ringing incessantly with people going in and out. She hadn't budgeted for a *car*. It would certainly eat a large hole in her capital, unless——

'Millie's, perhaps? Miss Millicent's?'

'It was sold to pay for incidentals at the finalising of her estate.'

'Oh. I see.' She swallowed. 'Well, I—I—naturally I'd get a car, of course. I can see that one would be more or less essential out here.'

'You hadn't expected to be quite so far out, in fact?' It was only half a question. The man was sure of his ground—unpleasantly so—and in any case her telltale flush must have told him all he wanted to know. His gaze was probing as he pursued his quarry a step further. 'You'd get an allowance, of course, for fostering the children. On the other hand, the Far-out Homes like to satisfy themselves that the foster-parent has an—er—a certain financial stability of his or her, preferably *their*, own. Are you with me?'

'With you?' Emmie blinked.

'You do understand what I'm getting at?'

Yes, she understood all right. Only too well.

'I believe, if I buy a second-hand car, and run the store with reasonable efficiency——'

Ridd Fenton got to his feet.

'I rather meant *without* the store,' he told her pointedly, coming over to where she too was now standing, and looking down at her blandly. 'The store is kaput. It's finished. Without our custom, that is—the Bruces' and mine. And I think I've already told you that we've transferred to Berroola Junction now.'

Emmie gazed up at him, her eyes wide. There was no mercy in that deeply tanned, granite face. None at all. His eyes were locked with hers, holding them in a penetrating, unwavering look that seemed to see right into her chaotically racing mind.

Without their custom——?

No, she'd never manage, and Emmie knew it. She had been banking on the weekly turnover from that propsperous little shop in that friendly little community. Without their custom——?

She was trapped. She had come to the end of the road. Or rather, into the corner where Riddley Fenton had been steadily nudging her.

It was useless to think of contacting Robert or Mark. They'd never back her up, or agree to her selling the stocks which her father had left her, or to buying her out of her share of the family home, or—or anything. They'd be like *he* was, this man here. They'd say she was nothing but a crazy child, that she'd better come back home and look after them again, and in return she'd have no financial responsibilities, they'd take care of that side, as they always had.

Emmie dropped her eyes, turning away. Her shoulders slumped.

'Without the store,' she admitted hollowly, 'I couldn't do it. I'd need to have the turnover. I'd been c-counting on it.'

Her voice thickened in a betraying way.

Emmie walked over to the window and stared out. She wasn't really seeing anything, just blinking into the darkness and fighting for control. It was the sheer hopelessness of defeat, the disappointment, that had brought her to this pass, she told herself miserably. To have got *this far*, and to know that you'd lost out, after all, was surely justification enough for a voice that had begun to wobble perilously, and eyes that stung with unshed tears.

'Emily?'

Ridd Fenton's hands came down on her shoulders and turned her towards him.

'Look at me,' he commanded, and Emmie had to raise her face and obey.

His image was misty, blurred. Just a wide-shouldered frame that blocked her shimmering vision.

'You want this very much.' The deep voice spoke above her. 'Why?'

'I—I've *told* you,' she murmured helplessly. 'The *children*——'

'Good God, girl!' The brown hands tightened roughly, gave her a sudden, savage little shake. 'That's no reason at all. At your age you should be thinking of having a family of your *own*— your *own* kids, not some motley bunch of half-nourished unfortunates whose mothers saw fit to dump them on a doorstep or foist them on an already long-suffering community practically the minute they were born. There are others to do that, Emily, older women, more Miss Millicents——'

'I—I *want* them,' she reiterated, passionately, hopelessly. 'Please?'

Oh, what was the use? She could see, by the set of the lean, hard jaw, the levelled mouth, that further argument would be fruitless. Emmie could only stare into Riddley Fenton's unrelenting countenance with eyes that were wide, misty, beseeching, dewy-lashed where clung the tears that she had no intention of allowing to fall. To cry would be unthinkable in front of *him*.

A tiny muscle flickered in his swarthy cheek.

'How do I know you'll stick to them?' he queried impatiently. 'What guarantee have I got that you won't go back to this chap who's got you acting crazy to get away just now? How can I be sure that you won't go tearing back into his arms as smartly as you ran out of them?'

'Oh, I wouldn't do *that*.'

'It happens, you know. A lovers' tiff, then forgiveness all round. The glorious reconciliation.' His eyes were hard, mocking—as mocking as the irony in his smoothly taunting voice. 'The younger they come, the harder they fall.'

Emmie's colour rose, and then faded, leaving her small oval face as pale and still as a gardenia bud.

'I can give you a categorical assurance that such a thing just isn't possible.'

You couldn't go back after a lovers' tiff if there'd been no lover in the first place, could you? The ludicrous ambiguity of her reply caused Emmie to smile wanly in spite of herself. She wasn't given to dallying with the truth like this, but he had asked for it, all along the line. She found that she was even deriving a certain bitter pleasure from deceiving him, since he was the sole, and intentional, stumbling block to her entire future here.

Riddley Fenton's eyes had narrowed. There was quite the strangest expression in them now.

Then, surprisingly, he smiled. It was the faintest of smiles, a twist of the lips merely.

'Well, Emily, in the face of that categorical assurance, I'm prepared to co-operate, but only up to a point.' He sighed resignedly. 'I'll list the goods you'll need to stock, and you can start up in business right away. I won't bother Sid Bruce in the meantime. I reckon Koolonga's requirements alone will keep the wheels turning for you, for a while at least.'

'You mean——?'

She was suddenly breathless as she tried to take in what he was saying.

'I mean that presumably you have sufficient capital to restock this store with supplies for Koolonga Station, plus enough sundries to deal with the odd traveller's demands. You won't even need to keep strictly to hours. Most people outback expect the stores to open up at any time they happen to be passing, in any case, so if you're actually living here, you'll be around.'

'Ridd—I——' She found that she could hardly speak for the sudden constriction in her throat. 'I don't know what to say. Th-thank you, Ridd.'

'You needn't thank me.' He was abrupt. 'Not yet. It mightn't last. Remember, you're strictly on approbation, for the *kids*' sakes. I know Sue doesn't want them on her hands for ever. If you default with them, you're out, though. It's as simple as that.'

He reached for his hat and gained the doorway. There he clapped the hat on his head at its familiar, concealing angle, turned.

'Oh, and—Emily?'

'Yes, Ridd?'

'Another thing——'

'Yes, Ridd?'

'Just remember that the customer is always right, will you?'

'*You* being the customer?'

White teeth flashed in the darkness of the doorway.

'Good girl,' approved Ridd Fenton, with maddening civility. 'You got it in one!'

And, gritting her teeth in a rush of pure irritation, Emmie heard him whistling softly as he went away.

She walked back to her chair, sank down into its faded depths.

It was humiliating to find that she was trembling. Hunger had left her. She leaned forward, head in hands, and forced herself to review the misery of her position.

How dreadful to be beholden to a man like Riddley Fenton! How vexing to find that your brave bid for a new and independent life had ended in such a compromise! To realise that without that man's reluctant offer to put business your way, you couldn't run this little store at all. To know that one slip—one *default*, he had said, hadn't he?—and you were out, just like that. Not out of the shop as a dwelling-place, of course. Not even he could force her out of there. But without an adequate income on the capital she was about to expend, there'd be no alternative but to give up, would there? They'd never let her keep the children, either, not when she couldn't even keep herself, and Millie had left them in her care, she was sure, although she hadn't actually said so, in so many words. She had bequeathed Emmie a moral legacy, along with this strange little broken-down shop, a trust to look after her orphan family for her and to keep that family together in happiness and love and security.

Security? She sighed. It *could* have been the most worthwhile thing Emmie had ever been able to do in the whole of her life—her dull, uneventfull, predictable life—couldn't it, if only Koolonga had been a warm-hearted, thriving country town, if only this store had been a dear little white house with beds of agapanthus and a wistaria and an apricot tree and a bell that rang all the time as people came and went. It *could* have been——

'Emily?'

The man's voice, speaking quietly right beside her, made her jerk her head up with a start of surprise.

Ridd Fenton was there. Back again, looking down at her.

'I thought you'd gone.' Her voice was dull.

'Obviously.' A pause. 'I just came back to tell you that I'm starting up the electric light plant, in case you happened to be startled by the sudden noise. I'll leave it charging all night, and switch it off in the morning when I'm passing. You needn't let my comings and goings disturb you. I'll be stopping it before you're even awake tomorrow, most likely. You can turn on the lights here in a few minutes, and put those Tilleys out, if you like.'

'Thank you, Ridd.'

He frowned. 'Nothing else worrying you, is there?'

Emmie lifted a pale, strained face, shook her head.

'Nothing, thank you.'

The man still stood above her for a moment, big, irresolute, his frown deepening.

'Well, get some grub inside you, for heaven's sake, and

don't sit there tearing yourself to pieces like this,' he advised her gruffly. 'No man's worth it, I can tell you that. But being you, you'll have to find out the hard way, no doubt.'

And then he was gone, away again through the shadowed doorway, and this time he wasn't whistling at all. Emmie heard his heavy steps sounding across the yard outside, and then the shattering noise of the engine as it leapt to life in its tiny shed.

Too weary (or too cowardly?) to resume her former line of thought, she got slowly out of her chair and went to cook her eggs and bacon.

On Thursday morning she caught the train at the siding. It was the train on which Riddley Fenton had planned to send her away, back to Sydney, but now Emmie only took the train as far as Berroola. At the Junction she got off, and when she returned that evening it wasn't by train at all, but in her very own truck.

Emmie's spirits lifted as she bumped her way over the graded dirt road in the ancient vehicle. She had had an unexpectedly successful day, and with the acquiring of her own personal transport her sense of independence had been given a moral boost. What was more, Berroola Junction had turned out to be a pleasant little town, with several extraordinarily wide, quiet streets flanked by shade trees, each one in its own small, netted enclosure. The shops had been quiet and spacious too, with great sweeps of wooden floor and a noticeable dearth of people. What customers there were had been openly curious, inclined to be friendly, and when Emmie had remarked on the emptiness around her, they had smiled kindly and explained that Saturday was the busy day around here, because it was the day when all the country people from the surrounding district came in to do their shopping.

Generally they made a day of it, she was told. There was a children's park and playground, a swimming-pool, bowling green and tennis courts, and on Saturdays all of these places as well as the shops were apparently swarming with life, although Emmie, faced with this enormous sense of space and silence, found it hard to believe.

Where, she wondered, did all the people come from, when outside Berroola there seemed to be only isolation and bare brown plains?

Well, they'd explained, when they said that the country people came 'in', they really meant that some of them came a very long way indeed, anything up to a hundred and fifty or so miles, some of them. The distance they had to travel to get there was partly the reason why they turned the occasion into a family social outing as well as a shopping expedition. The day was usually rounded off with a hearty meal with one's friends at the Greek café-restaurant or the new motel, and once a month there was an open-air cinema to which they could go. Then, at night, the family would all bundle into the car again and face the long drive home under the winking ceiling of stars. Not even the dust and the gates to be opened could diminish the perfection of their 'day in town'.

Emmie had spent her own 'day in town', and spent it to her satisfaction.

At least, she *thought* it had been to her satisfaction until this very moment in time, when there came a strange coughing noise from beneath the dusty bonnet of the pick-up. The vehicle gave several erratic lunges, ferocious enough to make Emmie grip the wheel in self-defence, and then it came to a final halt.

When she tried to start the engine again, there was a peculiar little knocking noise, and then nothing.

Oh dear. Whatever could have gone wrong?

She clambered out, wrestled with the rusty catch and raised the bonnet. Her eyes widened at the conglomeration of wires, tubes, plugs and oil-stained filters. She'd had no idea that an engine could look so complicated. Back there in Sydney, all she had ever had to do was drive it. Mark or Robert had always been the ones who lifted the lid and looked inside if Emmie thought she had reason to complain of the car's behaviour, and of course the garage had provided regular servicing too. Only once, when she broke down in George Street, had she had to deal with things alone, alone, that is, except for all the amateur mechanics who came flocking from the pavement to her assistance, arguing heatedly about their relevant theories as to what might have gone wrong. In no time at all someone had summoned a breakdown truck, and the offending car had been removed from her sight. It had only remained to her to take a taxi home and report the misadventure to Mark, who had contacted the garage and seen to all the ensuing ritual.

Here there were no taxis, no breakdown trucks, not even any passers-by.

Or were there?

Emmie stared at the moving trail of dust that heralded the approaching traveller, sank her teeth into her lip with vexation as she recognised Ridd Fenton's big Chev. It was a relief, when it got near enough to see, to learn that the driver was Kevin Condor, and not Ridd himself.

Kevin was alone. He pulled in ahead of her, got out from behind the wheel and came over.

'Good lord, is it really you, Emmie? What on earth are you doing in *that* thing?'

'Oh, Kev, am I glad to see you! It's my new car—truck, I mean.'

'New?'

'Look, Kevin, I'm stuck.'

'Yes, I can see that. I didn't think you'd be stopped here just to admire the scenery. Where on earth did you *get* it?'

Emmie swallowed her impatience.

'At a place called Gulliver's Travels. They specialise in second-hand sales.'

'I know it. Gulliver's Travels for GIANT Discounts. Out on the Nobdoo Road. They specialise, all right! Whatever took you there, Emmie, to that used-car dump?'

'Second-hand, not used.'

'*Very* used,' Kevin corrected her shortly, peering inside at the panel with distaste. 'Eighty-one thousand, she reads, but you can bet that's not the half of it. She'll be wound back, with the head off as many times as I've got fingers. Now, why did you go and choose a thing like this?'

'I—I hadn't enough money for something better, not if I wanted to lay in some stock for the store. And anyway, I thought a truck would be just the thing. Much better than a car. Children just love sitting in the back of an open utility, you know. They get the breeze, and it's so much more fun than being cooped up in a saloon.'

'Hmph!' Kevin's grunt was disparaging.

'Well, can't you *do* something?' Emmie was beginning to be annoyed. 'If all you've stopped for is to criticise, you'd better just get going again!'

'I'll try.' He grinned at her peevish tone. She was beginning to decide that he was almost as maddening as his own boss, when he disarmed her completely by adding an appeasing, 'Now, don't flap, and tell me what seemed to be wrong. Did she die on you?'

'Well, I—I changed gear, and it sort of jerked and stalled. And then I pressed the starter and nothing happened.'

'She's in gear now.' He slid into the seat. 'Second.'

'Fourth.'

'Second,' said Kevin firmly. 'She's been fitted with the four-speed optional, see. And a limited slip differential. Not a bad old bus, in her day.' He was mumbling to himself inside the cab.

'It's nice and roomy, anyway.' Emmie, posted at the window, took heart from his cautious word of praise, choosing to ignore that added 'in her day'.

He jabbed at the starter to no avail, climbed out again and peered under the bonnet.

'Ye gods, just as I thought! Your terminals are filthy!' he diagnosed in a disgusted voice. 'They might at least have cleaned them up for you!'

'Are they important?' she questioned humbly.

'Everything's important, when it makes a difference to going or *not* going. Really, Emmie'—Kev sounded exasperated—'you aren't fit to be let out alone. One should *never* buy a second-hand vehicle without a preliminary road test and a thorough going-over by an experienced mechanic. And some guarantees? No, they didn't give you any, you don't need to tell me.'

'I'm sorry, Kev, if I've been foolish. It was because of——'

'The money. I know. It's false economy though.' He shook his head, his fingers working deftly as he cleaned each terminal in turn. 'That should do it. She's contacting now. I'll top up the battery when we get you home. You start off, and I'll follow to make sure you arrive.'

'Thanks, Kev. And I'm sorry,' she said again, this time from the driver's seat, with the engine stirring heavily to life. 'It's not in bad order generally, is it?' Her eyes were round with anxiety. No guarantees, he'd assumed, and he was right. 'I mean, it's big and roomy, and substantial. *Strong.* I—I thought it would be just the thing.' Her voice tailed off.

Her companion put a hand up and patted her shoulder consolingly before he slammed the driver's door, shutting in her small, disconsolate form.

'So it *will* be just the thing. Don't worry too much.' He sounded kind. 'I'll give it a strip-down and get it purring like a baby for you yet.'

'Oh, Kevin, *would* you?'

'Haven't I just said so? At least I'll keep it in running order. More than that I can't really promise.'

'That's all I'll need, just running order,' she accepted gratefully. 'And—er—Kevin?'

'Yes, Emmie?'

'Would you mind awfully not saying anything to Ridd about my breaking down like this? He'd think me awfully stupid. I'm afraid he does already.'

'Not a word, if you want it that way. I'll be as silent as the

86

Sphinx itself,' he promised gravely, but she could see that his eyes were brimming with laughter, all the same.

Emmie let in the clutch and moved off, sighing resignedly.

It seemed that her day hadn't after all been quite as successful as she had hoped. Thank heaven Kev seemed to know what he was doing, and would get things right for her. She could see those men at Gulliver's Travels in Hades for selling her a dud, she really could! You couldn't trust a man an inch not to do you down if he got the chance, it seemed. A good thing that with any luck Ridd Fenton need never know. Bad enough to have Kevin Condor laughing, but Ridd——! No, thanks!

When she got home, she would wash and polish the bodywork. It was that nice bright blue that had taken her eye in the first place, and if Kevin could get the engine running better, the whole effect would be more impressive. It might even appear to be a reasonable purchase in Riddley Fenton's eyes, although she had no intention of ever letting him know how much she had paid for it. The suitability of a truck as opposed to a car was not to be gainsaid. Why, she could even take firewood home in the back, stock for the store, all sorts of things.

When they reached their destination, Emmie ran the truck into one of the open sheds at the rear of the store and climbed out. She was carrying her day's purchases towards the back door when the big Chev rolled up behind her. Kev had wisely been keeping far enough away to avoid her dust.

'Well, we made it!'

'Here, let me carry some of those.' He relieved her of the better part of her burden. 'You've been having quite a spree at the Junction, by the look of things. What in the name of all that's wonderful—no, it *can't* be——'

'A tree? It is. It's just little yet, though. An apricot,' she confirmed triumphantly.

'But why?'

'Because I've always wanted one, that's why,' she told him

stoutly. 'I've ordered a wistaria, too, but it isn't the right time of the year to transplant it, it seems.'

'Are you a keen gardener, then, Emmie? It's an uphill struggle out here, you know—light rainfall country, windy too in some seasons, when the dust-storms blow, and the bore water doesn't suit a lot of things.'

'That's why I didn't risk the agapanthus. I didn't even ask for them,' she replied reasonably. 'They're those lovely purple and white lilies, you know. They're a bit tender for here, I would think, so I'll have to be content with a wistaria and an apricot, won't I?' She was speaking half to herself, gazing out over the plain where a gilded sunset had turned the mulga clumps to molten gold, with eyes that were soft and dreamy all of a sudden.

'Will you?' Kev shot her a swift look, half puzzled, half indulgent.

'Yes, I should think so. But with the white walls——' Emmie put her parcels down on the step, and surveyed the dissolute rear of her inherited dwelling with eyes that were beginning to shine with enthusiasm. 'With white walls, and the wistaria climbing about the place, it will begin to look like—like *home*.'

'You're going to paint it?' He sounded doubtful.

'Why not?'

'No particular reason, I suppose, except that it's always been that dirty pink colour. Weatherboard is usually that colour, Emmie. Weatherboard colour. In any case, I'd question whether the surface is good enough to warrant new paint.'

'I'll scrape it and reprime it, and then it will be good enough. I've got stripper and everything in that parcel you're carrying, as a matter of fact. And the paint's still in the utility.'

'You think it will be worth all that trouble?'

'Oh yes, Kev, it'll be worth it. Just think, the lovely little store with its white walls and the purple wistaria rambling about, and the—no, not the agapanthus, after all—but an apricot tree, with real, fresh apricots that you can pick warm off the branches.'

'You could do that over at Koolonga,' Kevin informed her sensibly. 'There are fully a dozen apricot trees in the orchard there, and Ridd wouldn't mind.'

Ridd!

No, she didn't want Ridd's apricots. She didn't want *anything* else from Ridd. She was beholden to him already, just for being here. He had taken some delight in making his point over that. Without his custom there'd be no turnover. Without a turnover, no income. Without an income, no security. Without security, no children. Without the children, no mission in life. It was as simple as that!

'I want my *own* apricot tree,' she avowed with such feeling that Kev looked closely at her again.

'What a strange little thing you are, Emmie Montfort. And look! What's this?'

He deposited her things down on the kitchen table, and rattled a box-like shape done up in brown paper. From within came a throaty, tinkling sound.

'That's my bell—a little bell for the shop door. The kind that rings every time anyone goes in and out. I couldn't get a proper one. They told me that one's for a ringer-horse or something, but it will do.'

Kevin's face was a study.

'Who'll be going in and out? I mean——' He scratched his head rather helplessly.

'If nobody else is, *I* will be,' Emmie informed him firmly. 'I'll come in by the front whenever I'm out, and the little bell will tinkle a welcome, just the same as it would for proper customers.'

Kevin took her by the shoulders, and looked down at her with that belying twinkle.

'Know what I think, Emmie Montfort?' he stated solemnly. 'I think you're loco.' He tapped his head comically. 'Loco—but in the cutest way.'

Then they both burst out laughing.

And in fact, as they sat down amongst the parcels to partake of the tea that Emmie had quickly prepared, they were still giggling like a pair of children.

CHAPTER FIVE

EMMIE applied herself diligently during those next few days.

It was hot work, scraping off the peeling paint and sandpapering the rough places in preparation for the fresh white coat the weatherboard was about to receive. By the weekend she had completed all but the back of the lean-to, and it was while she was daubing stripper on to the shabby exterior that Susan Wensley came to call.

Emmie was quite certain that it was Susan Wensley even before the other girl climbed out of her Holden sedan and came over to where Emmie was stooped over her task.

'You must be Emily Montfort.' The girl extended her hand. 'Sue Wensley.'

'Oh yes. How do you do?'

Emmie ran a rather grubby hand down her paint-streaked overall before extending it to meet a cool, confident clasp.

'Ridd suggested that I'd better come over and make your acquaintance, and that's why I'm here,' Susan told her with smiling candour. 'I'd have come under my own steam sooner or later, I suppose, but my weekends are rather precious to me, as a matter of fact. Teaching full-time is a demanding occupation, and one gets to look forward to one's few hours of uninterrupted leisure.'

'Yes, I'm sure. Do come in, won't you?' Emmie put the brush down and beckoned her visitor inside. 'I'll just get cleaned up, if you'll excuse me a moment, and then I'm sure you'll be glad of a cup of tea. I'm dying for one myself.'

She ran to her room and whisked off the stained overall in some haste. One felt at a distinct disadvantage, like this, beside that lithe, comely figure out there. Susan's own cotton dress was the prettiest coral colour, uncreased, unmarked, her thonged sandals the latest fashion in footwear. With that abundant dark hair and wonderful violet eyes, her colouring, and stature too, could almost have been classic Montfort—the sort of Montfort that earned those lingering looks of admiration from the male fraternity. No wonder Kevin Condor had apparently found her irresistible. And Ridd Fenton, too.

Emmie pulled on her own floral cotton and smoothed her hair, gazed for one despairing second at her little-girl reflection in the mirror before she went back to where Susan Wensley was flicking with disinterest through a magazine while she waited.

The juvenile reflection hadn't lied, worst luck.

'Are you *really* twenty-six? You look about sixteen, if you ask me,' Emmie was told with a frown almost of disapproval. 'I must say the petite are at a distinct advantage in that respect—men are apt to go all gentle and protective over you little five-footers when all the time you're as well equipped as the rest of us to take care of yourselves.' She followed her hostess through to the kitchen, and perched idly on a corner of the table while Emmie put the kettle on. Emmie found herself rather liking the other girl's naturalness, and somehow couldn't resent those frank remarks.

'I suppose none of us is satisfied with ourselves,' she smiled. 'It's a universal feminine failing. It's five foot two, actually, by the way. I've always longed to be taller, and as for protectiveness, I've been smothered with it all my life. You take my advice and treasure those extra six inches. They can mean that one doesn't have to fight quite so hard for one's independence.'

'Who wants independence?' Susan shrugged. 'It's an overvalued commodity.' She reached into the biscuit tin and helped herself, sank firm white teeth into the gingernut she had taken. 'We all thought Miss Millicent would have chosen someone a little more—well, *mature*, to take on her responsibilities with those children. You're a bit of a surprise, you know. To Ridd too. He almost thinks they'd be better to go back to the Homes and take their chance there, but he tells me you're obsessed with the idea of having them.'

Emmie flushed.

'I want to give them a home, yes, that's true. Millie was my friend, our old governess for years and years, you know. I think it's just what she'd have expected me to do, no more, no less. It's not a question of sacrifice on my part—I must stress that point.' She passed the other her tea-cup, offered biscuits again from the tin. 'I genuinely *want* to have those children. I think I can give them the continuity and security that Millie hoped would go on even though she herself wasn't here.'

'I see.' Susan crossed her legs and sipped her tea thoughtfully. They were very attractive legs, long and brown and shapely. 'Ridd gave me the impression that you were so fervent about it that you'd probably be over to get them almost immediately. I was rather surprised that you hadn't come. I've been expecting you.'

'I wanted to get the place in order just a little bit first, before I got in touch. I've only just got delivery of my car, too. And I've been planting out a few things. I thought it was important to get this painting done, as well, before I got them over.' She laughed. 'Children and the permanent variety of paint don't mix awfully well, at least not in my experience, and I did want it all to be fresh and bright and welcoming for them when I got them back. As a matter of fact'—she hesitated only an instant—'I *did* suggest to Kevin that he go on and tell you that I'd arrived and would be coming for them soon, but he—he had other things to do, and couldn't.'

'Kevin Condor? Yes, I'm *sure* he had,' Susan agreed dryly. Then, after a pause, and looking absorbedly at the tip of her painted toenail, 'How *was* Kevin, by the way?'

'Oh, very well, really—at least so far as I would know. He's very nice, isn't he? Kind. He was to me, anyway, over at Koolonga. And he was very obliging driving me over here with all my stuff.'

'Was that all he said? Just that he had other things to do?'

'More or less.' Had there been some subtle change in that cool, disinterested voice? 'I think that was about all. He said he'd leave it to Ridd to tell you. And I suppose he was right there. I mean, it *is* Ridd's affair more than Kev's, being the executor of Millie's estate and all.'

'That's not why he did it, for all that, Emily.' Sue Wensley's eyes were hard and bright as she put down her cup and looked directly at Emmie.

'He was quite sincere, if that's what you're questioning.'

'He did it to hurt me, that's all.'

'Why would he want to hurt you, Sue? You don't mind if I call you Sue?'

'Of course not. In fact, if you're going to be here for any length of time, I hope we can be friends. It's nice to find another girl about one's own age in the vicinity. You may have heard that I—lost my husband—rather precipitately——'

'Yes. I'm sorry.'

'Well, it isn't easy, I can tell you, Emily, that first while of adjustment after the shock, the awfulness, the sudden emptiness and loneliness.'

'No, it must be dreadful,' agreed Emmie with feeling. 'I can only begin to imagine it, I'm afraid. But surely you're wrong about Kevin. I mean——'

'I'm not wrong,' Sue sighed. 'The trouble with Kevin is that he can never forgive me for turning to other people when *he* wasn't here. Well, what did he expect me to do? Try to get through it alone? There are times when one just can't do that, and for me that was one of them.'

'I'm sure he understands that, though. He strikes me as being a very understanding person. Reasonable, too.'

'He understands *nothing*. He doesn't even try.'

'Oh, surely? I mean——'

'Kevin's changed,' the other girl asserted bluntly. 'You wouldn't understand, Emily, because you never knew him before, but when he came back to the country he was different. Not the Kevin I'd known before. A stranger.'

'Well, I suppose those new experiences would be bound to affect one, wouldn't they? I mean, one would be bound to change just a little, going through all that.' For some reason, Emmie found herself leaping to Kev's defence. Who was this girl to judge? What did *she* know about the rigorous demands of military training in strange places, the difference in routine and environment, the pain of being parted from the person one loved? Had she no imagination, no understanding herself? Or was she being stubborn, believing only what she *wanted* to believe, because it made her feel more comfortable in her relationship with Riddley Fenton? Easy to say that someone had changed, when it suited you to think so, and justified your own inclinations. Poor Kev! 'If he seems different, it will only be a surface thing, I'm sure. People don't change basically—not when they've been fond of each other.'

'Who said anything about being *fond* of each other?' Sue Wensley's tone was brusque. '*Fond?* What does that mean, anyway? Nothing lasts, Emily, you'll find that out for yourself some day. Nothing endures, specially if we want it to very particularly. Nothing lasts. Life's for living, hour by hour, and day by day. Just take it as it comes, that's my motto. Grab what happiness you're offered, while you can, that's what I say now. We're all changing, and so is life, with every minute that passes. Time doesn't stand still, so we can't either.'

'Physically, that's true. I can't argue that we don't all grow physically older, and in that sense change, with the passing of each day and the passage of time. That's nothing more than the natural sequence of evolution itself. But not so far as our love and feelings go, Sue. It's a state of mind as well as a physical state, love. Perhaps in Kevin's case only the outward manifestation has been altered by his experiences. Have you thought of the possibility of that?'

'My dear, you're impossibly naïve, if you really believe such nonsense. Let's leave it, anyway. What you think can't make a mite of difference to anything. I was just curious to

95

know how Kevin's mind is ticking these days, that's all, but I'm not actually terribly interested. One can't go back to how things were, even if one wanted to, and I *don't* want to, as it happens. Having been married, I've evolved a stage further than Kevin, if we're going to talk about evolution in any sense. And now, having been forced to stand on my own feet, I've emerged as a person who has little time for that possessive, jealous calf-love that young men go in for—the sort that can abandon the so-called loved one to go off with the chaps in khaki just for the hell of it, little boys playing at their eternal game of soldiers. I prefer to receive only what I'm prepared to put into a relationship, and only an older man is willing to meet one on those terms, I find.'

She must mean Ridd Fenton, mustn't she? It certainly figured. He was the sort of man who'd find Susan's philosophy attractive, no doubt. No ties, no commitments, just a cold-blooded 'affair' that was conveniently suitable to both the involved parties. What a callous creature he was, if ever there was one, especially when poor Kevin was emotionally implicated, too. Ridd would need to be blind if he couldn't see that much! Blind, and selfish. Very much the latter, most likely. She could hear his voice now, as if he were right beside her. 'No man is worth it,' he had said. No woman, either, in the reverse situation. Ridd would never tear himself to pieces over a woman. This convenient affair with Susan Wensley would suit him down to the ground. No soul-searing emotion, no entanglement from which he couldn't easily extricate himself in a manner at which he was by now no doubt adept. And all the time poor Kevin suffered—inarticulate, miserable.

'Are you sure you are being fair to Kevin?' she persisted. She didn't want to appear presumptuous, yet she was consumed by a burning pity for the boy.

'More than fair.' The other's voice was brittle. 'It's amusing that he didn't come on that day, though, to tell me you'd be coming for the kids. Typical. It's his way of punishing me for getting married to Jo in the first place, I suppose. Well, what did he expect me to do? Sit around and languish when he chose to go off and play at heroes?'

'The going-off wasn't of *his* choosing.'

Susan sighed.

'That's just where you're wrong, Emily. There are a lot of things that you don't know, so do stay out of it like a pet, will you?' She put down her cup, stood up. At the doorway she paused, as if obliged to explain further.

'Kev could have got turned down, or at least a deferment. There were medical grounds, if he'd cared to pursue them and use them to his advantage. Oh, nothing serious—a chest condition that sometimes comes on. Others have got themselves turned down for less, but he wouldn't even try. Not even for *my* sake.'

'I see,' said Emmie gently, and strangely enough, it was compassion and not contempt that she felt for this lithe, beautiful, mixed-up girl as she followed her out and over to her car.

An impasse between two likeable people. Deadlock. And Riddley Fenton had been quick to step in and take his chance.

'I'll come over for the children tomorrow, if that will be all right, Sue?'

'I've prepared them. They're quite looking forward to returning with you, I think. After all, this *was* their home, such as it is.' She leaned out of her window and surveyed the store with fresh interest. 'I must say you've improved the old place already, Emily. Does Ridd know you're doing this?'

'Not unless Kevin told him.'

'Kevin knows?'

Emmie nodded.

'He came over yesterday and helped me to scrape off some of the harder bits,' she admitted, and was surprised to see the look that flitted over the other girl's expressive features.

'Oh. So it's not just at *Koolonga* that he's been kind?' An eyebrow lifted, as Susan tapped a manicured hand upon the steering-wheel with a gesture that was difficult to define.

'Well, I'd better be getting along. Come for tea, and you'll be able to size each other up over a plate of scones or something. About four o'clock, if that suits. I've a pile of exercises to correct yet, so there'll be nothing much in the way of a spread, I warn you.'

'I'll be there.'

Emmie watched the Holden until it was lost in its own dust-cloud, and then she went back to her pail and brush. She had been happy enough at her task before, but oddly, Sue Wensley's visit had depressed her.

She forced herself to carry on until darkness fell, and finally went inside to light the chip heater for her bath, wondering why she should react like this. It was nothing to do with her, after all, and tomorrow she was going to get the children back to Millie's little house, now white and shining and smelling strongly of fresh paint. *That* should be enough to chase away any fleeting sense of depression, surely?

The school building was larger than Emmie had expected it to be. It was constructed of the seemingly ubiquitous weatherboard in the same colour as her own little store had been before its coating of fresh white paint. A fading caramel-pink. Weatherboard colour. There was a netted area that enclosed a roughly laid-out tennis court, some swings and a wooden see-saw. At one end was a long, low, open shed that might have housed bicycles, horses, or in fact almost anything. Today it was empty, and silence reigned in its vicinity.

Emmie walked up the path to the open door. From inside came the sound of voices—children's voices.

As she stood uncertainly on the step and tapped on the door frame to announce her presence, there was a shriek of excitement from somewhere within.

'Here she is, Miss. It's *her*!'

'All right, then, Jim. I'm coming in a minute.'

Three faces peered around the corner of the dark passage, three pairs of eyes surveyed the newcomer with cautious curiosity.

Blue eyes. Blue again. And the last pair, great dark orbs that were liquid and beautiful, without the inquisitive, bird-like sharpness of those other pairs. Serene eyes. Melting brown pools of tranquillity and peace and quiet dignity.

'Go on, Daisy, girls first.'

Brown-eyes was unceremoniously shoved from behind, and catapulted into the hall, a thin little thing in a skimpy cotton smock. Emmie took in the delicate limbs, crimped black hair, smooth, milk-chocolate skin that told of mixed blood, part-Aboriginal.

'Daisy, did they say? Hullo, Daisy.'

She knelt down and put out her hands, and the child took them unhesitatingly.

'Hullo.' Daisy jerked her head behind her, to where scuffling noises and a few giggles were emerging.

'They're shy,' she explained equably.

'And you aren't?'

A shake of the curly head.

'I've been waiting for you to come all day.'

'That's nice. So have I. I've been counting the minutes. How old are you, Daisy?'

'Six. But Morrie and Jim are nine. My birthday's soon. Come *on*, you two.'

'Yes, go on, sillies.' That was Susan's voice. She came around the corner, smiling, herding the boys in front of her as she approached. 'Morris. And here's Jim,' she supplied. 'And I see you've already made Daisy's acquaintance.'

The boys extended tentative hands, prompted by their teacher. They wore neat khaki shorts and shirts, and their hands had obviously been recently in contact with some soap and warm water. Emmie took in the shining faces, slicked-down hair, scrubbed knees, and hid a smile. It wouldn't be like that for long, but it wasn't a bad start, all the same.

'Can we call you Emily?' asked Daisy solemnly, unabashed by the boys' shyness. 'We gotter call Sue "Miss" because the others do in class, see, but you're not our teacher, are you? You're just a friend.'

99

'I'd rather Emmie, actually, if you don't mind. It's what I'm used to.'

'It suits you better than the other,' said Susan unexpectedly. 'I'll call you that, too, if you prefer it. Come on round to the veranda and we'll have tea there. It's cooler.'

It was a gay affair. In no time at all the boys had forgotten their initial malaise, and fought over the pikelets and the final drop of lemon syrup as if Emmie had been amongst them all her life. Daisy belied her serenity by running about in a mercurial fashion, up and down the long veranda and in and out the swing-door, favouring her foster-brothers with a flashing white smile that teased and taunted as she plucked the last pikelet from under their very noses with her thin, supple, milk-chocolate fingers, and darted off.

'Whoopee!' Morris stopped in mid-pursuit as he spied the old blue utility. 'Can we ride in the back going home?'—and there was a sudden lump in Emmie's throat as she lifted Daisy into her arms and set her in the back beside the boys.

'No standing up, then. The first one who tries it comes in front.'

She turned to Susan, who was reminding her erstwhile charges that she expected to see them in class in the morning, and not to be late.

'Thanks for the tea and everything, Sue.'

'Don't mention it. I enjoyed it myself.' Susan gave one of those careless shrugs whose genuineness Emmie already felt inclined to question. 'Don't let these little monsters devour you, will you? And you be good for Emmie, now, you kids. And I'll see you tomorrow. On *time*, remember.'

'Yes, Miss,' they choroused, and then Emmie found first gear and they were bouncing up and down in the back and waving to their teacher as the old truck headed out on to the track.

When she stopped at the front of the store they all scrambled out and dropped nimbly to the dusty ground.

There was a sudden silence. Then—

'Skin the lizards! You've painted it!'

'Crikey. It—it looks different!' Morris and Jim gazed in awe.

'Do you like it?' asked Emmie uncertainly. Perhaps it would have been wiser to warn them first that she had made some alterations.

'It's great. You'd hardly know the old place, would you, Jim? Look, she's fixed the veranda rail, too.'

'No, Kevin did that. I'm afraid carpentry is hardly my line.'

'Can we sleep on the veranda? We always *do*?'

'Do you?'—doubtfully.

'Sure. On the stretchers. The bedroom's too stuffy.'

'I don't like the veranda,' put in Daisy firmly. 'You have to have mosquito nets, and they're stuffier than the bedrooms.'

'They're not, stupid.'

'They are.'

'They aren't!'

'I wish Millie was here,' said Daisy stormily, and all of a sudden she began to cry. She cried with great, heart-shaking sobs that shuddered right through her thin little frame and caused hot crystal tears to course down her smooth brown cheeks.

'Cry-baby-cry-put-your-finger-in-your-eye.'

'Be *quiet*, Jim! Here, Daisy'—Emmie scooped the little girl up and held her close. 'You boys can carry in your things—Daisy's too. Hurry up, now.'

She walked away with her sobbing bundle, out of earshot, patting Daisy's heaving back as she clasped her to her and murmured soothing words into the curls that tickled her own cheek.

'Did you call her Millie too, Daisy? So did I. We all did, from the time I was just a little girl, much smaller than you even. I wish she was here, too, just as you do, but we can't do anything about it, and she'd *hate* us to cry. She wanted us all to be happy, and that's why she brought us together like this. Look, I've something to show you, something I want you to see.' She set the child down gently.

'What is it?' Daisy sniffed.

'An apricot tree.'

'It hasn't any apricots.'

'It will have, though. It takes time, just as it takes time to get used to not having Millie, time for you and me and the boys to get to know each other, time for us to become real friends. *Everything* takes times, Daisy. We have to be patient, and everything will work out happily for us all.'

'When will it have apricots?'

'When it's big. It's only little yet, as you can see. We'll have to keep it watered so that the roots don't dry out, and then it will flourish and grow, and one day there'll be real fruit on it. You and I will have to carry water to it every day at first, until it gets used to being here. It's no more at home here than I am yet, you see. This soil is strange to it. But if we look after it regularly and tenderly, every day, it will feel firmer and more secure as time goes on, and one day it will be a beautiful, strong tree. So we mustn't forget to look after it. I'm depending on you to help me.'

Another sniff.

'Do you know something, Daisy?'

'What?'

'Millie always wanted an apricot tree. When I was just about your age, she would tell me often about the little place she dreamed of having one day—a dear little house with white walls and an apricot tree.'

'Why didn't she, then?'

'Because she was much too busy looking after you and Jim and Morris, I suppose. *You* were more important to her than they were, you see, and with the store and everything there wouldn't have been time. But I think she'd be pleased, don't you, about the pretty white weatherboard and the apricot tree, even if it's only a little one yet?'

Daisy's sobs had ceased. Except for an occasional almost inaudible hiccup, she had stopped crying.

'Can we have hundreds-and-thousands on our bread at

tea?' she asked unexpectedly, with a child's unpredictable change of mood. 'There's a whole jar of them in the pantry.'

'Yes, I'm sure you can. We all will, probably. I haven't had them for years myself.'

Emmie smiled, and they walked into the house together.

Suddenly she felt a lifting of the heart, as if she too had returned to those tender years of hundreds-and-thousands and wobbly jellies and an ability to scrap one's grief with a swift, complete abandonment before the tears were even dry.

They settled down successfully after that. Indeed, the months that followed were some of the happiest of Emmie's whole life. Her relationship with the children developed into one that could only be described as 'sisterly.' To herself she admitted that she must still be a child at heart, for she found herself positively enjoying their games and enterprises, the treks in search of grubs and chrysalises and locusts, the expeditions to the water-hole where the birds flocked, the fishing sorties in an effort to lure the mudbrown yabbies from their haunts in the only deep remaining pool in the Berroola Creek some distance away and trap them in the fat-baited tins which Jim and Morris had prepared for the purpose. It was fun to pack a picnic, load up the rusty old truck with grid-iron and billycan, and chops and freshly made loaves, and depart for the day with the 'family' chattering their approval and excitement as they helped her to get ready, and then to depart in a meandering course over the wide plains country, without any particular goal in mind.

Each day promised a new adventure, something to remember. A strange flower in the scrub, an unfamiliar bird flitting through the quandongs, a swarm of wild bees zooming over a patch of needlebush to their nest in a hollow tree—the 'sugar-bag' beloved of the dark people. Daisy knew as if by instinct where to find these things, although her tenderest years had been spent at a mission station and then the Far-out Homes. She had the quick humour of her mother's race, the endless patience that enabled her to squat motionless for hours, observing the ways and wonders of nature. The comings and goings of a bed of ants could keep her entranced for an entire morning. She would spend an afternoon quite happily, lying on her tummy over the green, slow water of the creek, watching the delvings of the carp amongst the weeds beneath the surface—as still and silent as a small, prone, dusky statue—and she would oblige the boys in their search for bait by pulling back the bark on certain saplings, reaching in with thin, quick fingers to bring forth the fat yellow grubs that were hiding there, almost as if she had known—had *always* known—just where they lurked. She was better than Emmie at making the little flat johnnie-cakes that could be cooked so deliciously in the ashes of the camp-fire, and her ear was always the first to hear the sound of the approaching animal, the initial sigh that presaged a whirlwind, her eye the first to note the changing colour of the air before a dust-storm, or the birds' sudden swerve in direction as they swooped down to water at some undiscovered gilgai.

It was Daisy, today, who sat up first and listened to the slight crackle of a horse's hooves picking their way delicately through the scrub to their side. The boys were making twig drawings in the dust, and Emmie was lying on the dry leaves in the shade with the shantung-baku hat over her head.

When she, too, heard the sound of the horse drawing nearer, she removed the hat and sat up.

Ridd Fenton was the horseman. The animal was his powerful bay stallion. When it broke through the scrub into the clearing, its rider halted it and waited there a moment, a broad-shouldered figure sitting easily in the saddle, hat down in that concealing way he had, reins clasped carelessly in one hand as he surveyed the little party.

' 'Lo, Ridd.' Morris scrambled to his feet. 'Can I take Rufus?'

'O.K., mate.' With a single, graceful movement the man swung down to the ground, a long-legged tree of a man, he seemed, from Emmie's sitting position, in wash-pale moleskins that hugged his narrow hips, and the familiar, dusty elastic-sides. 'Over to that stringybark, then—and remember the hitch I showed you last time.'

'I will, Ridd.'

'It won't kick him or anything, will it?' Emmie twisted the hat between her fingers anxiously.

'Rufus?' Ridd shook his head. 'He's quiet enough if he's handled right.' He removed his hat, and squatted at her side. 'Never sap a kid's confidence in handling an animal until he does something that gives you reason to, Emily. Rule number one. If you do, he starts off nervous, and that makes the animal wary too. They're quick to recognise the confident touch. That goes for horses, dogs, cattle-beasts, the lot.' He shot her a swift look. 'You don't ride?'

She flushed.

'I've never had the chance to learn, I'm afraid.'

Again that look—a slightly more unnerving one, this time.

'I thought perhaps that was what Kevin was making those frequent visits to the store for—to teach you. He's around quite a bit these days, isn't he?'

Emmie stood up. Her face was hot, and not simply with the heat of the day.

'He comes to—to service the utility, and look after it for me. He's very good with engines and things,' she added lamely. 'That's why I asked him to do the electric light plant too. We don't use much, and I thought it would save you calling in as well. You don't *mind*, do you?'

The wide shoulders shrugged.

'Why should I mind? As you say, it saves a call. Where did you get that utility, by the way?'

'In Berroola.'

'Naturally. But *where* in Berroola?'

'I really can't remember.' Emmie sounded vague, kneeling down again on the dry leaves and gathering together the picnic pannikins.

'Hmm.'

Ridd's grey eyes were half-closed in that lazy, contemplative manner that prevented one from knowing just whether he believed one or not.

'You're still too thin, Emily,' he commented now, critically. 'Tell me, are you happy, now that you've got your way?'

'My way?'

'Over the kids. And the store.'

'Oh. Oh *yes*, Ridd. Very happy, thank you.'

'You don't regret your decision, then? No—er—no nagging, tender memories that keep you awake in the night?'

'You're trespassing, I think,' she murmured evasively, closing up as she always did at any hint of a reference to her past, different though it was to the one that *he* imagined! 'Are you still cutting scrub for those sheep of yours?'

He nodded, almost absent-mindedly, as though having to drag his thoughts towards the answering of her questions.

'That's right. And will be for some time, by the look of that sky. If we even got a slight fall of rain, you'd be surprised how the green would appear, though. Even without a follow-up, they'd get a temporary pick, and if they were a bit stronger I'd move them nearer the homestead block.'

'You haven't been out there today?'

'I've been repairing a mill. I was riding back when I saw the smoke and reckoned I'd better check. Did those bushes and other spares come in yet, Emily?'

'Not yet. I'll give them to Kev as soon as they do.' She stood up again, pushing back her hair, aware that his features had tightened. 'I'm sorry if the smoke worried you, Ridd. We're always terribly careful, as you can see—right in the middle of a bare place, and we always "kill" the ashes before we go.'

He didn't reply, just stood there frowning.

It seemed to Emmie that Ridd was *always* frowning when she was around. It was only for Susan that he kept that sudden, tender, boyish grin that could flash out so surprisingly, grooving his tanned cheeks and crinkling his far-seeing eyes into laughing indulgence. For Susan, that is, *and* for the children. He was doing it right now, for Daisy, in fact, grinning down at her good-naturedly as she tugged at his trousers and cried,

'Take me on Rufus, Ridd, please? Please, Ridd, take me up on Rufus? I *like* Rufus, don't you?'

Brown fingers tweaked the mop of curls.

'O.K., Daisy. But just for a minute, mind. Reckon I've got a lot of things still to do.' He was untying the reins from the branch where Morris had looped them, talking to the children as he did so. 'How's Bingo?'

Bingo was the kelpie pup that he had given to Jim and Morris to train.

'He's coming on. He's not too bad, really. He can bring back a stick and everything now, Ridd, and he's doing what we order more, too. Where's Fritz?'

That was Ridd's own blue cattle dog which was usually to be found trotting endlessly in the wake of his master and the handsome bay stallion. Today Fritz wasn't here.

'He got a cat-head in his off hind pad, and went lame on me, so I left him at home today.' Ridd was lifting Daisy into the saddle, and now he swung up behind her. 'Talking of cat-heads brings me to cats. Susan tells me you found a stray at the schoolhouse the other day and took it home, is that right? I hope it's healthy, is it? You haven't landed Emily with some disease-ridden nuisance?'

'Oh *no*,' they chorused protestingly. 'Emmie didn't mind, did you, Emmie?'

'No, truly.' Emmie reinforced the point. 'She's the dearest little cat. Black as night, and affectionate too. And she was needing friends, so I was glad they brought her. We call her Quinty—Daisy named her that.'

'Quinty, eh? Do you know what that means in the aboriginal tongue, Emily?' There was a softness in Ridd's eyes as they asked the question from his saddle-height above her—a softness that the children must have put there.

'It means "plenty", doesn't it? Daisy told me that too,

didn't you, darling? And we called her Quinty because she was so thin and poor, and every time I was getting her something to eat they all kept saying "Give her *plenty*, Emmie, give her *plenty*." Isn't that right, Jim?'

'S'right, Ridd. We thought it was a bit different, see. I mean, different from Darkie and Blackie or any of them ones.'

'*Those* ones.'

'Yeah, *those* ones. I mean, everybody calls black cats Darkie and Blackie. There must be millions of 'em in the world already, but I bet there's only one Quinty, and that's our one.'

'Yes, I'll bet.' Ridd was smiling now. In front of him Daisy was beginning to wriggle. 'Come on then, Rufus. Round the block and back again.'

He didn't need to dig his heels into Rufus's flanks to make him leap forward, Emmie noticed with some apprehension. The big animal had been stamping and sidling impatiently, straining at his curb all the time that Ridd had been talking to them. She watched as the great creature pounded away from her as if unleased from a troublesome prison. The man who rode him was moving with the animal, long-legged in the stirrup, hat pulled down again, with one muscular brown forearm enclosing Daisy's small, skinny frame in an enveloping clasp.

When they came out of the stand of timber and on to the open plain, Ridd put the stallion to a full gallop, and then horse and rider and passenger were one rhythmic form of grace and speed as Rufus stretched out to show his paces. From where she waited at the edge of the scrub Emmie could catch Daisy's childish cry of pure ecstasy from the safety of that encircling arm, and when they returned and finally came to a frothing halt beside her, she could see that the little girl's face was glistening with the excitement of that exhilarating experience, her eyes alight with joy.

Ridd handed her to the ground from his seat in the saddle.

'Like to try?'

'What? Now?' Emmie was startled.

'I wouldn't let you fall, Emily.' Ridd's tone was grave, but there was an unexpectedly teasing gleam in his narrowed grey eyes.

'No, thanks, I couldn't possibly.'

She couldn't *possibly*! What? Sit up there like a six-year-old, with that man's sinewy arm slung right around her? Pulling her back against his broad, exposed, open-shirted chest until it looked as if it were just *one* passenger seated up there in Rufus's saddle? Never!

'Another time, maybe.'

He shrugged offhandedly, but she could tell by his expression that her face was as scarlet and uncomfortable as it indeed felt, and that this fact merely added to his amusement.

How she hated that man, she told herself as he raised the slanting hat and then allowed Rufus to amble away at a quick, restless gait without even bothering to look back and wave. You never knew where you were with Riddley Fenton, not in the way you did with Kev, for instance.

Dear Kev! How kind he had been to her, ever since she had arrived. True to his word, he came along regularly to check over the truck for oil, tyre pressure, all the things she knew nothing about. And it had been her own idea that he might keep an eye on the electric light plant, since he was around already anyway. It didn't take long, and it was a way of avoiding Ridd Fenton's uncomfortable presence except for those rare times when he actually came himself for something he wanted from the store.

There was little doubt which of the two men the children welcomed most.

They liked Ridd's teasing attentions, found it difficult to understand Kev's reserved manner, his grave kindliness that hid that endless preoccupation with his own personal problems. Sometimes he would ask cautiously for Susan, but mostly he didn't mention her. When he did enquire, it was almost agonising to see him working carefully around to the subject, setting the verbal scene, as it were, for the casual question which Emmie guessed was certainly anything but unimportant.

Emmie's heart ached for him. Ached for them both, in fact.

She had grown to appreciate that there were lots of likeable things about Susan once you sifted out the brittle remarks and small sarcasms, once you penetrated that hard, protective shell which she had adopted.

Two perfectly nice people, who had somehow lost each other in life's rocky way.

A pity, that, and it was most unlikely that they would ever come together now—not now that Riddley Fenton was on the scene.

Emmie could hardly pretend, not even just to herself, that the man was without attraction. A sort of *animal* attraction, it was. The kind that made you just a little breathless when he pinned you under that confounding grey gaze. The kind that caused your pulses to flutter in an annoying and inconvenient manner when his work-rough brown fingers happened to come into contact with yours as you both went for the same article on the same store shelf at the same moment. The kind that sent a warming glow right through you when that level mouth lifted in a word of praise—rare moment, indeed!—or jerked your heart almost to a stop when it chose to actually put on one of those sudden, uncomplicated, eye-crinkling smiles.

Yes, Riddley Fenton was a—well, a peculiarly attractive man, she supposed, even when he didn't care very much for one and therefore didn't even bother to try. When he actually set *out* to be attractive, as he no doubt did with Susan Wensley, he must be positively devastating!

Poor Kevin! He didn't have a chance against *that* sort of competition!

Emmie stood on the outskirts of the timber until the horse and man were just a single, moving dot on the horizon, and then, sighing, she turned and went back through the trees to the picnic clearing.

CHAPTER SIX

IT was at the end of the following week that Kevin invited them all to go to town.

'No school tomorrow, so how about it? I'll come over early and we'll make a day of it.'

'Well——' Emmie hesitated, observed the shining expectancy on three young faces, and made up her mind. 'We'd like that, Kev, wouldn't we, children? Thanks very much.'

'That's settled, then. It will have to be the jeep, I'm afraid. Ridd will be off himself in the Chev, or I know he wouldn't mind me using it.'

'Is he going away?' Emmie did not mean to sound hopeful, but life would be a lot more comfortable without Ridd Fenton's background presence and the possibility of his always turning up in the wrong place at the wrong time, which he had a positive knack of doing. He hadn't been away on a single one of those plane trips of his, not since the day she had arrived, so surely one must be in the offing by now?

Kevin's expression had set.

'He and Susan are going off somewhere, I believe,' he informed her tonelessly. 'She hasn't been away for a while, so I suppose she feels she's due a change, and week-ends are her only chance until the holidays. I've no idea where they're going, though, so don't ask me.'

'I wasn't meaning to pry, in any case,' Emmie reproved him a little uncomfortably, and then brightened purposefully. 'That will be lovely, anyway, Kev, and we shall look forward to it. We can take the truck on from here, and you can leave the jeep. There'll be more room, and you might even drive it for me.'

'That'll do, then, Emm. See you in the morning, nine o'clock-ish.'

He left them, then, to embark on their session of hair-washing and excited preparations, and when he returned for them next morning they were already waiting on the small front veranda, and needed no second bidding to clamber into the utility.

It was an idyllic day. What was left of the morning was spent in wandering idly about the stores, which were this time thronged with people. Kevin seemed to know most of them, these visitors to town, and took obvious pleasure in introducing her to his friends. Emmie was glad that she had worn her prettiest dress and that her hair was clean and soft and shining. It gave her the confidence she needed to meet the openly critical looks which she was receiving.

She was aware that she was something of a curiosity in Berroola Junction today. Most of the people whom she met had heard that someone new had come to the store and had taken back Miss Millicent's children, but Emmie sensed that her appearance had somehow taken them by surprise. They huddled in little groups talking and looking after her when she had left them, and she found that the only way to cover the faint embarrassment she experienced was to turn her attention to the children themselves. Consequently, she indulged them rather more than she had intended, buying them small items that they admired without argument, chatting animatedly to them as she herded her small party from shop to shop, while trying to ignore the inquisitive glances and subdued conversations that were going on around her.

They lunched at the café on steak and eggs, and ice-cream sodas, and after that they strolled down to the play-park.

When sufficient time had elapsed after the meal, the three children elected to go swimming, and Kevin and Emmie lay in the shade on the grass nearby, talking desultorily.

It was a pleasant spot in which to relax. Other people already occupied the scattered benches or wandered down the paths beside the river. Small children ran and skipped tirelessly over the lawns and amongst the flowers, ignoring the notices that warned them to keep off the beds of geraniums and cannas, petunia and snapdragons that made such a colourful display. From the pool came shrieks of laughter and the endless sound of splashing.

This atmosphere was good for Kev, thought Emmie to herself, playing with a blade of grass which she had plucked, and watching his face as he lay there with his eyes closed. Some of the strain had gone, and his brow was smooth just now, unfurrowed by the tormenting thoughts that were never far away. She was glad, now, that she had come after all, since the outing seemed to be having a therapeutic effect upon her companion, and the children were obviously enjoying every minute of it.

'Want to swim?'

'I don't think I can be bothered,' she confessed lazily. 'And anyway, I didn't bring my costume.'

'You could hire one, I suppose. Used you to, in Sydney?'

'What? Swim? Not much. My sisters did, though. I'm not very good, I'm afraid. Not the athletic type at all, in fact.'

'Don't apologise for that, Emmie, as if it's something to be ashamed of. You're very nice the way you are, if you ask me. Sort of cosy, companionable, easy to be with.'

'Thanks, I must say.' She hadn't meant to sound tart. It was just that—well, there were so many things she'd have liked to be called rather than any of those. They were homely attributes, quite run-of-the-mill. Very ordinary indeed. Wistfully she couldn't help reflecting how nice it would be, just once, to be told something just a little more exciting about oneself than that one was cosy, companionable and easy to be with.

'Now I've offended you, and I didn't mean to.' Kevin sat up, put an arm around her. 'Dear Emmie! Can't you see that it's a compliment, what I'm saying? You're a girl in a million, if you want to know. Who else could I possibly have told about Sue and me, for instance? Who else would ever have bothered to listen, let alone understand? Who but you

114

would have——'

'Kevin, look !' Emmie interrupted in a voice that had gone strangely dry. 'Those people over there, talking by that willow—isn't it Ridd and Susan who are with them? Yes, it is ! And I'm sure they've seen us.'

She tried to draw away.

'Well, what of it?' Kev sounded stubborn. His hand remained exactly where it was, albeit his fingers had tightened somewhat convulsively. 'It's a public park, and everyone's in town, it seems, so they've as much right to be here as we have.'

'Yes, it isn't that. I just thought——' She broke off to stand up, thereby forcing her companion to withdraw his arm and stand up too. 'I—I really think I should get those children out,' she muttered confusedly. 'They've been in the water long enough.'

'O.K.' He brushed the grass clippings from her back as he spoke. 'I'll wring out their cozzies while you get Daisy dressed. Then we'll go and get a drink. I thought we might try the motel later.'

Emmie's face was flushed.

'Kev, I really think we should be thinking of getting home. At least the children and I should—so I'm afraid that means you, too, since we're all in the same vehicle.'

'What's the hurry, for heaven's sake? You're enjoying it, aren't you?'

'Oh yes, it isn't that. It's been a marvellous day out, but I don't want to be home too late. They'll be sitting in the back in the dark and everything. Look, Kev'—she turned to him persuasively—'why don't we all come back to my place, and I'll cook us a special meal? We'll take a vote to find out what to have, and if we haven't already got the makings in the larder, we'll go and buy them right now, before we go. What do you say?'

'I wanted to save you that, Emm. Hang it all, you do it every day in life, as far as I can see. This was to be a treat, and they give a very good dinner at the motel, too.'

'Another time, Kevin. Please. This will be a treat, too. I love cooking special things, and it's ages since I have. Let's go and get something tasty and madly exotic, and I'll show you how good I am. It'll be fun, and we can do the motel another time.'

'If you say so, then. But I don't suppose the children will plump for anything exotic, anyway, so I reckon you're being over-hopeful. I insist on buying whatever it is you decide on, though. This was to be my treat, remember. We'll get some wine too.' He was beginning to sound slightly more enthusiastic, and Emmie knew that she had won.

She was not sure, quite, what had caused this feeling of almost blind panic, but it could hardly be described as reasonable. It had gripped her so precipitately that it had allowed her no time to analyse the cause. She only knew that she suddenly felt stifled, confined, and that all she wanted was to get away from Berroola Junction as quickly as possible.

They shopped for the provisions they needed, hastened on by Emmie herself, and after another round of iced drinks in tall, cool glasses, they headed out on to the Koolonga road once more. Passing the driveway into the motel, Emmie somehow couldn't refrain from scrutinising the car-park furtively. No sign of a big, long Chevrolet, but that didn't mean that it most probably wouldn't be there later! Ah well, it was no business of hers, really, was it? It could have been embarrassing for Kev, though, she told herself stubbornly, and then chided herself for going to such ridiculous lengths to justify her own sudden, childish whim to escape.

Back at the store they unloaded their purchases. Emmie rinsed the swimming things and hung them out on the line, and then went inside again to prepare dinner, while the children chattered animatedly about their day's adventures and then took Kevin off to show him Quinty.

'*If* we can find her. I think she's often away hunting when she's not actually in the shed. She must be a good mouser. She's getting awfully fat.'

'Why Quinty?'

'It means plenty, you see. She was thin when we called her that, and she needed plenty of tucker to rally her round.'

'Hmm. Maybe you'll have to change her name.'

'No, we won't. It's still all right, because now it could mean that there's plenty of *her*. Plenty of *cat*, I mean.'

'Which there undoubtedly is.'

Their voices receded and Emmie smiled faintly to herself as she got on with her preparations.

Chicken Maryland had won the vote, and it took her a while to do all the trimmings—small, puffy corn fritters, sliced fingers of banana, croquettes of potato, and the golden joints of meat.

When it was ready, she called everyone to the table, and they sat down—just like a proper family, she told herself, with Kevin at one end, and Emmie at the other, and the children at the sides. She had gone to special pains this evening, and her reward was in the wonder on the children's faces as they took in the pretty cloth, tall glasses of lemonade, and centrepiece of flowers.

Kevin raised his wine-glass in salute, and the two adults exchanged solemn glances.

'To us.'

'To us *all*,' affirmed Emmie, glowing with pleasure that the treat seemed to have turned out exactly as she had hoped.

Later, when the young ones had gone to bed, they sat on the front veranda making idle conversation, replete, tired, but strangely at peace with each other. Kevin lounged in the deck-chair smoking, and Emmie sat on the stool she had brought from inside earlier, listening to the occasional creak of the boys' stretchers around the corner as they turned in their sleep, lulled into somnolence herself by the intermittent shrilling of a cicada from somewhere out there in the bushes.

It was only when the long, dark shape of a car came over the level crossing higher up, and swept down the track past the store, catching the Koolonga jeep in its headlights' beams, that Kev finally got to his feet, stretched reluctantly.

'Good lord, I'd better be going, Emmie. I'd no idea it was so late.'

The car had of course been Ridd's. It took the left fork beyond the store, because he would be dropping Susan off before he returned to his own homestead. He must have seen the jeep that Kevin had borrowed still standing outside the store, but there wasn't much he could say, was there, when he was so late abroad himself?

Even so, Emmie found that some of the pleasure had gone out of the evening, simply with the passing of that long, sleek automobile.

She waved Kevin off, and went back to the kitchen, began automatically to put things away. She wasn't going to spoil a lovely day by allowing herself to think about someone like Ridd Fenton!

Next morning Emmie started to do up Daisy's room. The little girl had had her way on the night she had arrived, and only the boys now slept under the hooped mosquito nets on the veranda. Daisy had the small room adjoining Emmie's all to herself, and it had recently occurred to Emmie that it would be nice if the child could have a pretty, feminine little place of her very own—the sort of frilly, flowery sanctuary for which every small girl secretly hankers.

Daisy had been delighted at the prospect, and yesterday they had chosen delicate pale grey paper for the walls and some dainty rose-sprayed cotton for the bedspread and cushions to complement it.

It took longer than she had thought to paint the woodwork alone. The window-frames were old, and tiresome to do, and she had to putty them up in places where the wood itself was decaying. Poor old store! Underneath the surface brightness she had given it, it was in pretty poor shape!

By the third afternoon the boys were bored with the whole affair. When they came back from school to the tea that was waiting, they groaned when they saw the rolls of paper strewn everywhere and the kitchen table cleared for yet

118

another glueing operation.

'We thought it'd be finished by now,' wailed Jim.

'How much longer?' queried Morris. 'I'm sick of the smell of that stuff. What a fuss, and all because she's a *girl*.'

'Shut up, Morrie!' flared Daisy. 'Just because you're jealous, 'cos you aren't getting a pretty room of your own——'

'Jealous! Huh!'

'Children, children!' Emmie clapped her hands sternly, silencing them. To tell the truth, she was sick of it herself, but equally she was determined to complete the job. Poor kids! She could concede their point. The place reeked of adhesive, and there were scraps and trimmings lying everywhere. It would take her hours to clear up this mess even when she had finished the actual papering. There was glue on her hands, her clothes, her hair, not to mention all the other places it shouldn't be, and she was keeping her temper with difficulty.

'Look,' she said a little desperately, 'why don't you play something? Something—er—new?'

'Such as——?' Three pairs of eyes sought inspiration from the dark-fringed hazel ones up there on the ladder.

'Oh, I don't know——' Emmie gestured vaguely.

'We've played everything we can think of,' complained Morris. 'You said you'd take us over in the truck to see our yabbie traps. If *you* could come——'

'But I can't. I know, why not dress up or something like that?'

'Dressing up's for girls.'

'Nonsense! It's for everybody at your age. You sound about a hundred, instead of nine years old, talking like that,' she reproved. 'It's only for laughs, anyway. There are some things in the store cupboard that you could use—they must have been there since long before Millie's time even—they're terribly old-fashioned. And I've some funny old hats that you can put on.' She scrambled down from her perch to show them. 'See. You can do what you like with them, act out a play or one of your school stories, or make up something, anything. Go on, surely the three of you can think of something to do with all that! I shouldn't be long in finishing, if you can amuse yourselves in the meantime.'

'Oh, all right, then.'

The boys were slow to capitulate, but Daisy was typically enthusiastic. After they had disappeared for a while, sounds of pure merriment emanated from the bedroom. There were occasional long silences, each one followed by more gigglings and whisperings.

That little ploy seemed to have met with some success, thought Emmie thankfully, as she toiled with the long strips of paper and the gigantic brush. Her shoulders ached and her head felt as if it might snap right off if she had to move it even a fraction further back, but if she could—just—get—that—bit—there——

She was on top, the very top step of the ladder, leaning backwards at a perilous angle while trying to persuade two adjacent strips to match each other, when the little bell at the front of the shop chuckled throatily. When it repeated its tinny tinkling sound several more times she knew it must be the children. Jim was *forever* tinkling at that bell!

'You're busy.'

Ridd's voice, so deep and unexpected, right at her back, almost sent her flying off the ladder. She recovered her balance by a freak series of contortions, more athletic ones than she had ever dreamed she could produce! She glared down at him reproachfully.

'You frightened me,' she accused severely.

'I'm sorry.' He didn't sound a bit regretful, actually. Just amused. 'I'm a bit scared myself, to tell you the truth.'

'Why?' She pushed her hair back with glue-daubed fingers.

'Have you looked in the mirror lately?' He grinned, in that peculiarly engaging manner that had a slightly disturbing effect upon one's equilibrium. 'Come down off your perch and be human for a minute. You look like a small, distracted, warlike bird hovering about up there.'

'I beg your pardon.' She stiffened her voice to counteract that maddening thud in her chest, and climbed down carefully, ignoring the brown outstretched hand. 'Did you want something from the store?' she asked politely, pleased at the indifference in her tone. He need never guess the precise effect his presence so often had upon her, if she could maintain such an impartial pose as this always!

'The number seven wire, remember? Or haven't you got it yet, Emily?'

'Yes, it's in.' She knelt down at the dark counter, and pulled out the rolls from underneath. 'Here you are, Ridd.'

But Ridd wasn't looking. He was back at the door, inspecting the bell again. It gave a couple more of its bronchial chinks as his fingers pushed it to and fro.

'Do you stock these things?'

'Did you want some? They aren't for doors, really. They're——'

'For horses. I know.' He was looking at her strangely, and Emmie slid her eyes away, suddenly confused by the softening of his stern expression, the curving of the level mouth. 'Ringers and horse-tailers and spare-boys need them, certainly, but you won't get many of them passing here with their plants, Emily. This is predominantly sheep country, you see.'

'That's the only one I have, anyway, and it's not for sale, although I could of course order, if anyone happened to need any.'

'You bought it for this specific purpose? I hadn't noticed it before.'

'You always come in the back way, that's why.'

'So does almost everyone, so why bother with a thing like this?'

'Because I like it, that's why.' Her head went back defiantly. 'It's cheerful and welcoming, and it—it makes the shop sound busy.'

'As busy as you envisaged it?' Ridd's swarthy face was set in faintly critical lines. 'I'm afraid it doesn't ring as often as you'd imagined it might when you first pursued this hare-brained scheme, does it, eh?' He stood above her, twirling his broad-brimmed hat between his hands, searching her face in that uncomfortably penetrating way. 'How are things panning out, Emily? Financially, I mean, of course. Are you managing to tie the ends together?'

'Very well, thank you, Ridd. Very well indeed.'

'Hmm. Well, if there are any problems at any time, be sure to come to me, understand, rather than ask anyone *else* to tackle them for you.'

Now what did he mean by that, spoken in just that particular way?

'I—I'm not sure that I do,' she returned, suddenly—inexplicably—a little nervous of this entire conversation.

His mouth tightened perceptibly.

'I just want to remind you that I am virtually your guarantor, so far as this—er—operation is concerned.' He cast a disparaging glance around him. 'If you're encountering any difficulties, I'd like to know about them. Do I make myself clear?'

'*Financial* difficulties, you mean?' Her eyes rounded wistfully with the voicing of her own question. Wouldn't it be wonderful if she could have approached him, just now, on Kev's behalf? Dear, sad, inarticulate Kev! Wouldn't it have been marvellous if she could point out to Ridd how unfair his own association with Susan was, in the light of the younger man's prior claim? If she could only tell him how miserable he was making that other man! If she could only beg him to do the decent thing, just this once, and withhold that fatal, calculating charm of his, withdraw from the lists, give Kevin his chance to talk her round, even maybe to make up.

The stern features congealed.

'Financial difficulties, of course,' agreed Ridd Fenton smoothly, stooping to place the rolls of wire over his shoulder before turning to the door again. 'I haven't found you exactly receptive to any advice I've been able to offer in other spheres, so I won't presume to invite defiance of it again,' he observed crushingly, and Emmie knew that her sudden temptation to confide had been no more than a crazy notion, born of some strange, inexplicable, extraordinary impulse; it was better to allow it to pass unheeded in the circumstances.

A giggle from behind them made them both turn.

'Good grief, what's this? A circus, or Paddy's Market?'

Ridd's surprise was agreeably received by the strangely bedecked trio who confronted him. They pirouetted before him, patently rewarded by his mock admiration as his gaze travelled from the trailing skirts, coats, shawls and other dated details to the hats that were perched precariously on the heads of these ribald figures.

It seemed that he recognised that headgear instantly!

'Don't you mind?' he asked Emmie curiously.

'Mind? Why should I mind?' she laughed. 'It's keeping them amused while I finish Daisy's room, and far be it from me to knock any form of occupation that does that!'

'I didn't mean the form of occupation. I meant those hats.' Surprisingly Ridd's tone was sober now. 'You don't object to them getting bashed around like that?'

'Not in the least.' She shrugged, almost gaily.

'You would have minded at one time, Emily. In the beginning,' he pointed out. 'When you arrived here, you were guarding those things with your life.'

'That was then. Now is now.'

She shrugged again, would have turned away had not Ridd's hand suddenly clamped down on her arm, preventing her.

'What's so different about now? Why the change of heart?'

His grey eyes were speculative, waiting, as if in some way her answer might hold some peculiar sort of significance. How could it, though, over a few frivolous hats?

'Because my heart *has* changed, that's why,' Emmie told him hardily, refusing to be rattled by that vice-like grip. 'The past means nothing to me now. I'd never have believed that it was possible to batten it down so successfully, but I've discovered that if one finds enough present activity for one's mind and thoughts, the earlier things recede in importance. Those hats are related to the earlier things, so they're not important any more either.'

'I—see.' For some reason her reply was distasteful to Riddley Fenton. She knew it in the hardening glint in his lingering gaze, the disdainful twist of that expressive mouth.

He turned away abruptly, replaced his hat on his head, and shouldered his way out of the door with his load of wire, leaving the little bell jangling in his wake, and without even saying goodbye to the children.

At the jeep, he remedied this oversight.

'So long, kids!' he called, and lifted a hand in casual salute when he had thrown the rolls of wire into the back. But there wasn't a word for Emmie at all. Not a single word. Not a look.

Chastened, she stilled the bell's mad dancing and went back to Daisy's room.

It must have been a couple of weeks after that visit of Ridd's to the store that the rodeo came to town.

'It's half rodeo, half gymkhana,' Kevin explained to her when he invited them to accompany him. 'A lot of the locals go in for some of the horse events, but there are travelling professionals taking part, too, and you'll see some good displays of the bushman's traditional skills. I think you'd like it, Emmie, and it's something you should see. The children come from miles around, of course—it's a great day out for the youngsters.'

'We'd love that, Kev. We'll do as we did before, shall we? We'll take the truck, and you can drive.'

The gymkhana was held on one of the creek flats just outside Berroola Junction. By the time Emmie and Kevin and the children arrived, there was already a wide arc of cars, buggies, trucks, Blitzes, encircling the arena, and as they nudged their way into a parking space, a queue had formed behind them.

The two adults joined the throng of people who were either standing, squatting bushman-fashion, or sitting on benches around the safety rails, but Morris, Jim and Daisy found their view a better one from their elevation on top of the utility's dented cab. The next time Emmie looked round, they had been joined by a positive swarm of other children, all utilising the additional height of the back platform. Whether they had known each other before or not was hard to decide. They were all talking and pointing with animation at what was going on in the ring, with a child's quick capacity for forgetting such things as shyness or unfamiliarity in the excitement of a common interest. Watching the lively little group that crowded on to the old blue utility's rusted hulk under the mottled shade of the blue-gums, Emmie felt a lump come into her throat. How worthwhile it had been, this keeping together of Millie's 'family'. And how wise, after all, to choose a truck rather than a car, even if it *was* a rusted and unreliable affair for which she had probably paid far too much, and which certainly taxed even Kevin's ingenuity in maintaining it and keeping it on the road!

Emmie withdrew her gaze from the children, looked around her curiously. Away down to the right, past the lanes of spectators and the luncheon and beer tents, came the ringing echoes of axe on timber. It was evidently a woodchopping competition, and to her surprise the competitors were, without exception, women.

'Yes, you aren't seeing things. That's the Ladies' Woodchop. There's a nail-driving compo, too, if you'd care to go in for it?' Kevin smiled his amusement.

'No, thank you. They'd soon show me up, I'm afraid!' she told him ruefully, remembering her inexpert maiming of those branches she had gathered, and which she had somehow finally managed to mangle into pieces on her first afternoon at the store. Strangely enough, since that first time, she had never had to use the axe again, because in some mysterious manner, piles of neatly cut blocks seemed to materialise each day out of nowhere. They were always waiting for her in the shed at the back when she went out every morning to get wood to light the range. Emmie had known then, when she saw them, that she hadn't imagined the faint, dull, regular thuds in the soft dawn haze, when she was still muzzy with sleep, too drowsy to rouse herself to investigate.

When she thanked Kevin for his kindness, he had looked surprised and said 'Not guilty' in a quite convincing way. And when she mentioned it to Ridd he had simply shrugged, frowned down at her bare head in that scowling, intimidating manner, and growled, 'How often must I remind you, Emily, to always wear a hat? If I catch you out here again without one, there'll be some sort of trouble, understand?' and she had replied 'Yes, Ridd' so submissively that for an instant the scowl had threatened to give way to one of those intoxicating, curly smiles. Only he didn't let it, of course. Instead he strode off to where Rufus was waiting and swung up into the saddle in one single, quick, fluid movement that never failed to entrance Emmie when she was watching.

The actions of these horsemen in the ring just now reminded her of Ridd's.

They had the same controlled, graceful, athletic swing, the same supple body movement, as they raced at full gallop to cut out steers, or bent to pick up the trailing girth of a wild scrubber that had already flung its victim in the dust and was charging around in a blind scramble to get away from the unfamiliar smell of horse and human. Emmie found herself holding her breath in sheer dismay each time a contestant came plunging through the release-gate on one of these maddened animals, pivoting and jack-knifing in back-breaking succession, with spurs digging in and arm held high so that the judges could be assured that only one hand was clinging to the girth of the swivelling, pig-rooting creature.

The pace changed to a quieter one as the children now

filed in on fat-bellied ponies and proceeded to play Musical Chairs, and then went back to their own unfenced plot to engage in bending races, barrel events, trotting and other equestrian achievements, while the railed enclosure was taken over once more by those lean, sun-toughened men on their churning, galloping, cantering, propping mounts.

By noon, the bar and lunch-tent were swinging into action also, and a band of volunteers dealt with crowding diners and drinkers. Corned beef. Tomatoes out of wooden boxes. Hard-boiled eggs. Iced beer. Even tea, mugged out into pannikins from an enormous iron pot under which a wood fire burned and hissed continuously. All very civilised, marvelled Emmie, as she accepted some of the steaming brew, turned to speak to Kevin, and found that it was Ridd who stood there instead.

Ridd. And Susan.

'Oh! Er—hullo.'

Ridd raised his hat, but it was actually Susan who spoke first.

'Hullo, Emmie. I *thought* it was you from away around the other side, and then when I saw Daisy and Morrie on top of the truck, I knew you must be here somewhere. I suppose Kevin's around somewhere too?'

It was with a cool, studied carelessness that Susan looked about her for a moment before bringing her eyes back to Emmie's flushed face. How lovely she was today, in spite of that indolent pose. Tall and slender and very trim in immaculate jodhpurs and a crisp white shirt. Ridd had on a white shirt too, instead of the usual khaki. His sleeves were rolled, but he wore a tie in honour of the occasion. The tie had small green symbols on a geometric ground of brown and tan, and his brown forearms were the same colour as the ground of the tie as he folded them across his chest and looked down at her.

She gazed feverishly around for Kevin, but there was no sign of him.

Where on earth had he disappeared to, darn him? He'd

been here only minutes ago, and now she found herself experiencing a vague sense of panic and desertion.

'Yes, we're all here,' she replied a little defensively. 'Are you enjoying yourself, Sue?'

'Are you?'

'Yes, very much. It's all so—so *new* to me, remember. I've never seen anything like it before. And Kev's been very good explaining it all to me—the pick-up men, and what a scrubber is, and why they keep one hand up high, and—oh, loads of things I didn't know.'

'Yes, I'm sure he's very attentive.' Somehow Susan managed to alter the whole meaning of Emmie's innocent summing-up. She did it so subtly that perhaps only herself and Emmie were aware of the undercurrent, the innuendo. Certainly Ridd's expression remained inscrutable.

'Have you had lunch, Emily?' he enquired evenly, with his customary imperturbable politeness, apparently quite oblivious of the tension in the air. 'Would you like something to go along with that tea?'

'I've already had lunch, thank you, Ridd. I—we were just having a quick mug of tea before we went back to the ring. At least *I* was, and now I seem to have lost Kevin.'

'Too bad.' Susan's voice was creamy. 'I'm sure you'll manage to *find* him again, though, won't you, Emmie?' The girl turned, put a tentative hand on Ridd's brown forearm. Against the thickly-haired, teak-dark colour, that hand of Susan's looked honey-pale and smooth and somehow a little helpless.

'I'm so hungry, Ridd,' she asserted plaintively—and it didn't sound like Susan at all, somehow. 'Do you think we could eat now?'

'Yes, of course. You're sure you won't join us?'

When Emmie shook her head, he tipped the broad-brimmed hat and left her, and she finished her tea quickly and passed the mug back to the volunteer-helper. Those last few mouthfuls had tasted cold and bitter. They left an unpleasant dryness behind as she turned once more into the throng of people and walked slowly back to her position on the rails just in front of where the utility was parked.

The children shouted at her, and waved bottles of coloured lemonade aloft to show her that they were fending for themselves rather more than merely adequately. She smiled indulgently, but her thoughts were elsewhere.

Why had Kevin chosen that particular moment to disappear? What was the use of evading the issue in that manner? She was sure that that was the real reason for his hasty departure, and she was also certain that if he continued to dodge reality like that, he would never come to terms with himself. Such behaviour could only serve to aggravate the wound so that, at this rate, it might never heal.

She tackled him about it on the way home.

'Kookaburra singing in an old gum-tree-ee'—in the breezy back of the truck the children's voices were floating away, chanting the roundelay that they had learned at school—a round that Susan herself had probably taught them!

Snatches of the song came to Emmie as she broached the subject to Kevin in the front cab.

'I can't help feeling that Susan cares for you more than she dares to show, Kevin, do you know that? And even if she doesn't, what's to be gained by dashing off into the crowd like that?'

'I've told you, Emm, I didn't *dash*, as you put it.' He contradicted her patiently. 'I hadn't seen them coming when Bluey Rourke suggested that beer. And then, later—well, you seemed to be getting on all right, so I just left you to it. It would have been—intruding, to go back at that stage.'

'Intruding! How can you sit there and talk of *intruding*, when you happen to love the girl?'

'Who said anything about love?' Kev's expression was wooden as he swung the wheel to negotiate a rutted place in the road.

'*I* said it,' Emmie returned stoutly, finding that she was becoming angrier and more frustrated with each successive second, so unshakeable was Kevin's calm. 'It's time *one* of us said it, time *one* of us was honest about it.'

'Are you suggesting that I'm purposely ducking the truth?' he asked quietly. 'What a gutless crank you must take me for !'

She turned to him in quick distress.

'Oh, Kev, you know perfectly well that's not what I mean at all ! You're neither gutless *nor* a crank. On the contrary, I think up to now you've displayed a more than ordinary amount of courage in your life.'

'See the conquering hero comes? Medals and all?' There was a bitter twist to his mouth, so gaunt a cynicism that it hurt Emmie far more than if he had laughed openly or become really angry with *her*. 'Don't make the mistake of confusing heroism with obedience, Emmie. The one is a glorious compound of impulsiveness and crass stupidity, the other a somewhat characterless and compulsive wish for self-preservation that rather conveniently happens to coincide with ordered military combat-behaviour. When I was a kid in Melbourne my one idea was to get onto the land, Emmie. I never looked beyond that goal. And when Ridd offered me a place at Koolonga I reckoned I was the luckiest guy on earth. It was a dream come true, and you'll never know the wrench it was to have to leave. Suddenly everything I'd hoped for seemed to be snatched away. The radical change, the suddenness of it, the uncertainty, were pure hell. I couldn't adjust, though Heaven knows I tried.'

'Kev darling, I'm not talking about *then*,' Emmie chided him gently. 'I'm talking about *now*. About you and Sue. Remember?'

'It's all muddled up together, Emmie, whatever you say. You can't just divide your life up into neat compartments like you're trying to do, however much you'd like to.'

'It's only in your mind that it's muddled up, because of what happened to you and what happened to Sue. It's because it happened to her while you were away, can't you see that? Can't you see, the one thing was *then*, the other is *now*. One's past, the other present. Maybe even future,' she suggested softly. 'If you would only try a little harder to put the past behind you, and meet her on realistic, present-day terms.'

'I've told you, she doesn't give a rap.'

'She's not indifferent to you, whatever you may think.'

'What makes you say that?'

'I just have a—an instinctive knowledge of it. Women are intuitive about these things. We're good at reading other members of our sex. No, Kev, honestly, I wouldn't even talk about it if I didn't feel that somehow it's terribly important. To Susan too. To *both* of you. Whatever it is she feels—and I'm not clever enough to know what it is—it certainly isn't indifference. It's nothing so negative as that.' She slipped a quick glance his way, took in the set face, the whiteness of his knuckles tightening on the steering-wheel. 'It's something quite positive, Kev, something that's alive between you still. *I* don't know what it is, but *you* could find out.'

'How?'

'Don't ask *me* how, Kev!' She turned to him in pure exasperation. 'Don't ask *me* how you go about finding out! You do it how you used to do it, before any of this happened to either of you, you silly chump! You talk, you idiot! You *communicate*!'

'O.K., O.K., you little spitfire.' He put up a protecting hand in mock defence, with a glimmer of his usual gentle smile. 'Look, lay off, will you, Emmie? I've enough on my plate as it is, without you throwing any more crazy ideas into the melting-pot.'

'I'm sorry, Kev. I realise it's none of my business—it's just that I get so mad, seeing you two going on like this. All the same, will you do something about it?'

'I don't know. I'll see.' He smiled, faintly, noncommittally, and Emmie had to be content with that.

When he left them back at the store and said goodnight, Kevin's face still had that dazed, bewildered expression which her words had somehow managed to produce, and as she followed the children inside, she found that she was almost sorry that she had spoken at all. Sorry, because she might have been personally responsible for raising Kevin's hopes quite falsely. Perhaps it would have been better if she had made no mention of the matter at all.

Sighing, she reflected that perhaps it was a pity that she had ever gone to the rodeo with Kevin in the first place!

CHAPTER SEVEN

THE days continued in a pleasantly regulated manner. By now a certain routine had formulated itself—a routine that centred mainly around the children—getting them off to school each day, cooking their meals and packing their school lunches, washing and mending their clothes which, because of the incessant heat, were fortunately few, consisting mostly of shorts and shirts and a pleasing absence of socks.

Every morning Emmie stood at the front step with the shop bell still tinkling behind her and waved the three of them off. And every afternoon she stood in more or less the same place as she had in the morning, with the smell of the freshly baked tea she had made wafting from inside the store, shading her eyes against the sun and watching for the first figure to appear on the horizon. At that distance the children were nothing but tiny black indeterminate dots against the sky. One by one they would pop up beside the scraggy monument of ironbarks that crested the distant ridge, and then as the dots drew nearer they would emerge into proper figures with bobbing heads and swinging arms and moving, hastening brown legs. And by the time they got to the big yellow box tree where the track forked left, it became clear that two of the figures were spare-limbed khaki-clad boys, and the third a thin, mercurial, dusky little girl with a head of riotous black curls.

Emmie would wave, and they would all wave back, and presently the sound of their voices would drift on the still white sunshine right to where she waited—snippets of conversation, laughter, singing. Then, at the step, there was usually a cry of 'What's for tea, Emmie?' and a concerted rush for the door, where they delivered up their school satchels and followed that tantalising smell to its source.

After tea, as the sun sank low and the west blazed with colour, Emmie would often take Daisy with her as she filled a watering-can and walked around to the back to water the apricot tree.

It had taken root well. The leaves which had at first been wizened, and which had crackled dishearteningly beneath her fingers, had lost their furling edges and were fresh and dark and green. The trunk was straight and proud, and already it had sent out small sappy resilient branches.

It obviously liked being here, that apricot tree. It liked the small, white store beside the railway gates. It liked the scattering of sheds and the two lofty sugar gums, the yapping kelpie pup, the contentedly lazy cat, the three boisterous children.

It liked it here as much as Emmie herself. It was happy, and it must have decided that it wanted to live here too, since it had lost no time in thrusting its roots down further into the deep plains soil, so that it could shoot sturdily upwards and outwards in that satisfying manner.

Emmie knew exactly how many leaves and branches her apricot tree had. She counted them as they appeared, and sometimes she found herself talking to her little tree, almost as if it could understand what she was saying. It was a friend in which she could confide her happiness and contentment, and sometimes she could have sworn that its leaves whispered in a rustling reply. As its roots gulped down the pool of water that she poured carefully around its base, Bingo the pup would race round and round herself and the tree, as she stood there waiting for the water to go away, and when the water had completely disappeared, Quinty would come treading delicately along to rub herself back and forth against the staked stem before retiring to lick the mud from her paws. She did it, fastidiously, in the fading sun on the roof of the woodshed.

Even the boys would stop their scuffling and chasings

from time to time to come over and mark the small tree's progress. It was a routine which somehow managed to involve them all.

When the holidays began and the school was closed, Emmie found that life was more fun than ever before. Now there was any amount of time in which she and the children could explore and picnic, and they even began to lead her around on one of the fat, frisky ponies which Ridd had sent over from Koolonga to keep them amused. Jim and Daisy were accomplished riders, Morris slightly less daring, and Emmie most backward and cautious of all. She insisted upon having a saddle, saying that it gave her at least a measure of security. To her it was no joke to find oneself sitting bare-back on a pony that wouldn't stop trotting, feeling one's balance gradually slipping out of control, even though it wasn't far to fall.

When she invited Susan over for tea one day, the other girl chose to come over on horseback, and it was faintly discouraging to see what a splendidly composed and efficient figure she presented on her lively chestnut mare. Obviously the tailored riding outfit in which she had looked so smart at the gymkhana was not merely for decorative purposes.

'How pretty this little house looks, Emily, now that it's white.' Susan looped her reins over the post and followed her hostess indoors. 'You were right, after all, to paint it. One can see it shining in amongst the trees on the plain whenever one comes over the ridge. All it needs now is something done to the roof.'

'Yes, I thought that too. I've ordered some paint, in the same red as it had on long ago. I think it was red, don't you, that bit that's left? I shall have to borrow a ladder, though, to get up there.'

'Hmm. Perhaps Kevin might do it for you. He still helps around here a lot, I suppose?' It was difficult to detect what was behind that tone of Sue's, as usual.

'Sometimes, yes. And he keeps the truck running for me, quite wonderfully. I'm afraid I was badly taken in there, you know. I paid more than I should have for the wretched thing in the first place, but thanks to Kevin it hasn't been an altogether disastrous purchase. Do have a scone, Sue, or another sandwich?'

'Thanks.' Susan leaned back in her cane chair, munching absently for a moment. Then—'Strange that Kevin should be turning out to be quite an adequate prop of support, isn't it?'

'What do you mean by that?'

A shrug. 'Nothing too profound. Just what I say, really.'

Emmie put her tea-cup down carefully.

'If you mean that Kevin is a weakling, Sue, you couldn't be more wrong, you know. I thought you knew him better than that.'

For once, Susan had the grace to blush. Not a true blush, just a reluctant trace of colour, that crept uncomfortably up beneath the smooth honey-brown of her cheeks as she shrugged again.

'I know him better than anyone else, I should think.' There was reproof in her voice. 'That's why I'm surprised.'

'You *knew* him, you mean,' Emmie corrected firmly, gathering courage from somewhere and coming to an impulsive decision to be nothing other than frank. 'You knew the boy, but not the man, Sue. You haven't made the effort, you just keep saying he's changed and leaving it at that. You *knew* him, when you were both young and a little too selfish to study each other's real needs. But you don't know him now, Sue. You can't! Because, if you did, you'd also know how he feels—that he still cares for you, very deeply, and you wouldn't make those snide remarks and disparaging insinuations that you seem given to doing whenever his name crops up, whatever you may think of him.'

'You don't know what you're saying, Emily.'

'I do!'

Emmie stared back defiantly, as hot colour flowed into Susan's face. She appeared positively angry now—outraged and offended, too.

'I forbid you to discuss me with Kevin!' she said furiously. 'You overstep the mark, Emily, upon my word you do! You can do what you like with him, so far as I'm concerned, but just leave me out of your intimate little heart-to-heart discussions, understand? I refuse to have my name bandied about between the two of you, do you hear? And if you're foolish enough to believe all his confessions of undying devotion and self-pitying soul-barings, you're more stupid than I took you for! If he truly felt like that——'

She broke off, trembling, put down her cup and saucer with a shaking hand and walked over to the window, striving to control herself.

Emmie followed, placed a penitent hand on her shoulder.

'I'm sorry, Sue, truly. I had no right——'

'No, it's I who should apologise,' the other mumbled.

'It was unforgivable to mention it. You were a visitor, and at my own tea-table——'

'I shouldn't have gone off the handle like that, even so. A schoolmarm should never do such a thing. She's supposed to be virtually unshakeable.' Susan turned, smiled wanly, obviously having recovered her calm.

'I truly am sorry, all the same. It's none of my business, and of course I didn't mean to interfere or anything.' Emmie returned the smile a little anxiously. 'Have I spoiled our afternoon? I do hope not!'

'No, of course not.' There was conciliation in Susan's voice now. The level-headed schoolteacher part of her had supervened. 'You were talking of making a path to the front door, weren't you? Let's go and see, shall we, and you can tell me how you propose to do it.'

'Yes, let's.'

Emmie led the way thankfully, glad that the embarrassing moment was past. She pointed from the step.

'I thought I'd take it down to there, you see, right to the road. I don't know whether to edge it and have gravel, or perhaps to pave it with flagstones.'

'They're tricky to fit, my dear, and you'd need to lay them

with cement. Don't you think that's just a little bit ambitious? Why not sink the flags on their sides for edging, and have gravel in the middle? That would look suitably rustic, with half the effort and expense. You can get sandstone slabs in Berroola, and I'm sure Ridd would let you have a load of gravel.'

'How practical you are! Yes, that's the very thing.'

The two girls wandered about the precincts, discussing ways and means of improving the premises, and by the time Susan saddled up and rode off again, their relationship appeared to have regained its former cautiously friendly footing, much to Emmie's relief.

Indeed, Susan must have carried her goodwill a step further, because Emmie was only halfway through laying her flagstone edging when Ridd Fenton himself turned up, and already he appeared to know about her need for the gravel.

He must have ridden in from the south side, and tethered his horse at the back of the house, for Emmie didn't hear him approaching at all. He took her completely by surprise, striding around the side of the house just as she was staggering up the half-made pathway with a slab of sandstone clutched against her.

'Here, let me.' Ridd stepped forward and took the slab from her, frowning. 'That's no work for a woman, Emily. I thought I'd made it clear that you could come to me about anything like this. Where do you want it?'

'Just—here, if you—don't mind.' She was mortified to find that she was panting. But then she always *did* seem to be a little short of breath when Ridd was around! 'That's right. Thank you, Ridd. I'll check it before I firm it in, you see. I take the line and the level with that bit of string.'

He grunted.

'It's ridiculous you carrying these things yourself. I'll tell you what, I'll lay them in line for you, and you can do the levelling and go on from there later. And I think Susan said you could do with some gravel to finish the job.'

'Oh, she mentioned it, did she? I'd certainly be grateful, Ridd. You're both very kind.'

Another of those noncommittal grunts.

'You can fix me a nice cold beer, just to show your gratitude, if you like? Is there any ice in that shack of yours?'

'Plenty. And don't you dare call it a shack. When I've painted the roof again you won't know the place.'

'Good lord, is that the next thing?' He stood up, grinned. 'Go on, then, and bring me a decent-sized schooner, if you expect me to say I think that the roof's a good idea. I'm not sure that that iron isn't in too rusty a state, all the same.'

He was standing looking up thoughtfully at the iron in question when Emmie returned with the beer. It was a surprise, when he spoke next, that the subject was not the state of the roof at all.

'I was wondering'—said Ridd Fenton, removing his hat with one hand as he accepted the beer with the other—'if you'd like to come to a dance in town next Friday night?'

'A—a dance? *Me*?'

Emmie found her eyes widening, as they looked up into Ridd's face to see if he were joking. He didn't seem to be. The teasing glint was absent, for once. In fact, he appeared almost sombre, his grey eyes darkly shadowed and unreadable as he met her gaze unblinkingly. With his hat off, she could see the tiny beads of sweat clinging to his forehead, and the pale strip at his hairline where the hat stopped the sun from getting in. Where the strip was, there was also a faint red mark from the leather headband of the wide-brimmed hat, and his dark hair had been flattened damply against it. Emmie took in all these details while her mind was recovering from the sheer surprise of what he had said.

'That's right—a dance. Presumably you do dance, Emily? You're looking almost affronted. As if I'd made an improper suggestion.' His lips twitched.

'Oh no—I mean—yes—it's not *that*.'

'What, then?'

He drained the schooner, returned it to her, and wiped his lips with the back of his hand. Then he resettled the hat in position. Now she couldn't even see his eyes properly any more, so it was difficult to tell what he was thinking, especially as his deep, noncommittal voice did nothing to give him away.

'It's in aid of the Red Cross,' he told her evenly. 'A district thing. Everyone will be going to support it, and I think you should too. It's not a good idea to skip local charity events of this kind in a remote country area, Emily. People can get the wrong impression.'

'Oh, I see.' She felt somehow a little deflated at his matter-of-factness, although goodness knows why she should. It was something, surely, to have been invited by him at all! 'Well, of course I'd love to come,' she assured him dubiously, 'only I don't really see how I could. I—I'm afraid I mightn't have the right thing to wear. It's a long time since I—er—went to a dance.'

Her school-leaving social, to be precise, she could have told him. Emmie could see it in her mind's eye. The groups of excited girls, quite daringly turned out, staggering around in too-high heels and loads of unbecoming make-up. The boys, gauche and inarticulate, lining the opposite side of the hall. The eagle-eyed mistresses. The——

'What you wear is entirely unimportant.' Ridd brushed that aside with ease—with much more ease than those poor, awkward schoolboys could have done!—'I'm sure you'll find something. Anything goes at these affairs, you know. They're countrified, unsophisticated.'

'Well, there are still the children to be considered. I really don't think——'

'Mrs. Bexley can keep an eye on the youngsters. I've already arranged it,' he interposed. 'You can give her a shake-down here for the night, and then it won't matter how late we happen to be in returning. You needn't even wake her when you come in, and she in her turn needn't wait up either. I'll come over for her the next morning and take her back to the homestead.'

'I—see.' What a domineering creature he was! He had done all this arranging of his on the assumption that his invitation would be accepted! He hadn't even waited to see! Ridd Fenton was not evidently accustomed to his propositions being turned down, not where women were concerned, that is. What a conceited, autocratic man! Serve him right if she refused, after all. It would be worth it, just to see his face. That is, *if* she could see his face, under that concealing brim. Still, a dance was a dance, wasn't it? And it could possibly be quite an exciting evening, going to a country hop as Ridd Fenton's partner. Her senses were beginning to tingle treacherously at the mere prospect!

'You will?' The grey eyes were commanding—not *pleading*, as she could have wished!

'Well——' She hesitated for only a fraction of a second. 'Very well, I will. And—thank you very much, Ridd.'

'Don't mention it,' he drawled. 'The thing hardly gets off the ground before about nine o'clock. We'll call by at about seven for you.'

'We?'

'Kevin, and Susan and I. We might as well make it a foursome in the same vehicle, seeing we'll all be headed in the same direction,' he informed her carelessly.

'Oh, I see.'

And she *should* have seen! she chided herself fiercely, as she went back to the house after he had gone. She should have realised that of course someone like Riddley Fenton wouldn't be inviting *her* to a dance, as his very own partner. It had *seemed* impossible—deliciously impossible!—and that's just what it had turned out to be!

Suddenly Emmie found that she wanted to cry. It was stupid of her. Terribly silly, really. But that was what she felt like doing. Goodness knows why she should feel all churned up and confused like this, but she did. She also felt peculiarly flat and winded, as if she had fallen right on to her stomach from a very considerable height.

Ah, well. Crying didn't get anyone anywhere, so why even bother to begin?

Emmie shrugged resignedly and went instead to inspect her wardrobe to single out any possible candidates for the Red Cross dance in Berroola Junction.

When Friday night came round she had donned the only possible garment that would be even remotely suitable. It was a checked seersucker in muted tones of blue and grey and white. Unremarkable. Rather annoyingly juvenile, in fact. It made her hazel eyes glisten with the unenviable innocence of the schoolgirl she had been when last she wore it. Her hair, newly washed, silkily straight, had a 'classroom' cut and cleanliness about it, too. It framed her pale oval face in a way that made her long to sweep it away, up into something more exotic.

She longed, even more fervently, when she was handed into the back of the Chev beside Kevin, and saw how Susan's abundant dark tresses were piled on to the crown of her head, revealing a queenly neck and small neat ears from which dangled sapphire pendants the very same colour as the girl's eyes. When they all got out at the hall, Emmie could see that Susan's dress was white and starkly plain, full of impact. It was a perfect foil for her dark beauty and honey-toned complexion.

'Shall we go in?'

Kevin's voice was strained. As he took her arm and guided her in through the crowded doorway, it occurred to Emmie that perhaps this evening had been sprung on him in much the same way as it had been upon her. A Royal Command, one might almost have said! He had spoken noticeably little in the car coming in, and neither had she. It had been Susan and Ridd who had carried on an intermittent, relaxed sort of conversation in the front seat as the big car purred smoothly over the wide dirt road into town.

The hall had a structured steel framework with slabs of galvanised sheeting bolted to it to form the walls and high roof. A determined air of celebration was probably inspired by all those festive streamers that wound their giddy way up and down the supports and by the balloons that dangled in a myriad of gay colours from the ceiling.

Emmie tried to feel gay, too, found she couldn't. She felt ridiculously selfconscious and ill at ease, and all because Ridd Fenton had just walked into the hall behind her with the lovely, serene, poised young woman in white at his side.

Emmie dropped her eyes, noted with despair that the dull yellow lighting from the overhead bulbs had drained the last vestige of colour from the seersucker checks. They looked dispirited, limp, unutterably nondescript.

'Let's dance, Emm.'

Without even waiting for her assent, Kevin drew her on to the floor amongst the other rotating couples already there. Across the room she could see Ridd Fenton talking to a distinguished-looking elderly man, while Susan stood patiently beside him, smiling with faint indulgence as the two tall men became apparently more engrossed in what they had to say to each other. Sharon would have been able to stand there like that, too, just as Susan was doing, with the same measure of calm confidence, the same proud carriage. It must have something to do with knowing that one was beautiful, reflected Emmie sagely. In the same situation, she herself was invariably given to an attack of the fidgets!

'That's Selwyn Bruce,' Kev informed her as he whirled her past. 'He probably had to get here early to open the thing. He and Ridd are the big noises around here, you know.' He grinned reluctantly. 'If anything Ridd is bigger than Selwyn, but a good deal less noisy, if you get me.'

'Is there a Mrs. Bruce?'

'There've been three, no less, Emmie my sweet. What Selwyn lacks in actual acres he makes up for in wives. Maybe he reckoned that that put him one up on Ridd.'

'They're rivals?'

'All big pastoralists are rivals to some extent, Emmie. But they're good friends. He's a big, brash, noisy galoot, is Selwyn Bruce, but he's important too, and Ridd understands him O.K. They get along.'

'He manages him, you mean,' she accused resentfully.

'How do you mean?' Kevin was slightly startled at her vehemence.

'He *manages* him, because it suits him to, just the way he manages everybody. He studies them, he gets an insight, and then once he understands what makes particular people work, he starts to jerk the strings. He makes them dance to his tune.'

'Hey, aren't you being a little unfair?' Kev looked mildly amused at her fierce expression. 'What gives?'

'N-nothing. Maybe I just don't like big noises, that's all.' There was silence a moment. Then—'Kev?'

'Mm?'

'Kev, don't be angry if I say something, will you?'

'I can't promise till I hear what it is.'

'It's just a—a suggestion, really.' She looked up at him, soberly, willing him to take her seriously just this once. 'Kev, please ask Susan for the next dance.'

'What?' She had startled him this time, all right! 'For heaven's sake, why should I want to do that, Emmie, when I'm quite happy here with you?' he countered gallantly enough. 'Or am I such a rotten dancer that you're longing to escape already?'

'No, don't joke, Kev. Please?'

Her gravity had arrested him right in the middle of his gentle smile. It faded, half-uncertainly, and she felt his fingers tightening over her own although he obviously wasn't aware of the fact. The old, familiar, haunted look was back in Kevin's kind blue eyes, and Emmie was responsible! She thrust away a twinge of remorse, nodded encouragingly.

'Go on, Kev, do. To please me?'

'How would it please you?'

'It just would, that's all.'

'She'd turn me down flat.'

'Don't be silly! In front of all these people? Susan isn't the kind to make a scene.'

'That's a pretty poor reason for her to want to dance with me, Emmie, simply to avoid making a scene.' His voice was quiet, but she recognised the stubborn set of Kevin's jaw well enough.

'That won't be the reason,' she said, equally quietly. 'You'll see, Kev. You'll see just what I mean, I'm pretty sure you will. Honestly, Kevin darling, I wouldn't be urging you if I didn't have some—some—inner *knowledge*, now would I?'

'That feminine intuition?' He was smiling a little again, but it was a fairly unsuccessful smile, by and large.

'More than mere intuition. Something much more positive.'

'I—don't think I can, Emmie. I couldn't go through all that again!' There was real pain in his voice now, and she knew that the raw place had been reached.

'Isn't she worth it?' she whispered gently.

'Well, of *course* she's worth it! But——'

'Go on, then, Kev.' Her eyes were persuading him, pushing him on.

'What about you?' He was gruff, uncertain.

'I'm not a child. I can take care of myself.'

'All right, Emmie, I'll do it.' Kevin suddenly seemed to have given in. 'And then we can leave the subject once and for all, amen, for ever after, can't we?' he reminded her heavily, with a scowl that was not unreminiscent of Ridd's more minor ones.

'Go on.'

She gave him a little push away from her, stood watching as he squared his shoulders and threaded his way through the people to where Ridd and Susan were speaking to a few others. Even from where she was, Emmie could see Susan's small start of surprise. She found that she was actually holding her breath and clasping her hands together in an act of silent supplication, in case Susan should refuse. And then she expelled her breath again in relief, as Kevin took the tall, white, slender figure into his arms and moved out into the middle of the floor like a man in a trance.

Emmie glanced around, chose a seat beside a comfortable-looking matron in a violent floral dress and white platform sandals.

'Hullo, love. You're with the Koolonga party, aren't you? I recognised you instantly when you came in that door. Frank, I said—Frank's my hubby—Frank, I said, that's the girl over there, look. Don't you remember her, I said.'

'I—I'm afraid I don't recall—I haven't met you before, have I?' Emmie gazed rather helplessly into the florid face of her voluble companion. 'If I have you must forgive me. You see, I'm still a little strange. There are so many faces, you understand.'

'You don't remember? Surely you must! We sold you the truck, remember? Gulliver's Travels? That's my hubby over there, see. Frankie Gulliver.' The purple floral heaved and shook as she turned herself to point him out for Emmie. 'There—see!'—triumphantly.

'Why, yes, how stupid of me. I don't usually——'

'You don't mind if I take Miss Montfort away from you, I trust, Mrs. Gulliver?' Ridd Fenton's polite voice chipped in from somewhere above. 'Our dance, I believe, Emily.'

She felt his firm, imperious fingers warm upon her own, drawing her to her feet, and then she was swept adroitly into his arms, and the sight of Mrs. Gulliver's quivering, indignant face was entirely obliterated by Ridd's wide white shirt-front.

'You're trembling. Did that woman say something to upset you?'

'No, of course not.'

'What is it, then?'

'N-nothing,' she replied lamely, not sure that she even knew the answer for herself. He was an expert performer, but she was so overcome by nervousness that she seemed to have three feet tonight, and they all kept getting out of step.

When she had tripped for the second time, she said, 'Ridd,

I think I must be t-tired tonight. I—don't think I want to dance.'

'But you're going to, all the same.' His voice was almost dangerously calm, and his grip was like a vice. She couldn't have escaped even if she had tried. 'What's more,' he added tersely as he whirled her expertly into a cross-chassé and out again, 'you're going to enjoy it, or at least *look* as if you are.' His mouth relented a little. 'Come now, Emily, relax. It's not as bad as that, is it? Did you do much of this in Sydney?'

'Much of what, Ridd?'

'Dancing?'

'Oh—some,' she prevaricated, vaguely. It was easy to prevaricate tonight. She felt vague, unreal, in any case, as if she wasn't Emmie Montfort at all, but some frightened, lost, panicky little creature who suddenly found itself trapped in a place where it knew it didn't belong.

'—don't you think so?' Ridd's insistent voice reached her from somewhere in those mists of unreality.

'I—beg your pardon?'

His fingers tightened as he glanced down at her sharply.

'Aren't you feeling well, Emily?' He sounded grim.

'Yes, wonderfully well. In the pink. Never fitter. Why?'

'That's good. In that case, we'll have the next dance too. You're beginning to loosen up a little, I believe, so we may as well go on, even though you obviously find it an ordeal.' There was a biting sarcasm in his voice that made her turn her eyes upwards to his in bewilderment. Flint and steel could hardly have been colder.

They revolved, after that, in complete silence. Ridd guided her steps relentlessly, with expertise, and Emmie felt as if she were up there in the balloon-festooned rafters, watching woodenly from aloft, a helpless onlooker of this cruelly comic little farce. She moved automatically, sensing his directions, miserably aware that for some reason he was furiously angry. She found herself praying that the music would soon stop, and when it did she stumbled blindly to the chairs at the side of the room.

'I'll get you a drink.'

'Don't bother.'

'It's no trouble, I assure you.' That deadly, formal politeness again!

Emmie got up again, looked around wildly, and moved over to where a party of young people were talking on the opposite side of the room. They eyed her curiously, but with the unfailing courtesy of country people nevertheless allowed her to join them. She had managed to engage one of the girls in a rather feverish conversation, and when Ridd came back she succeeded in obscuring herself in the midst of the other group. She saw him looking around him, and then he presented her glass of squash, quite charmingly, to a perspiring dowager in pink who was sitting fanning herself, and shouldered his way through the crowd again.

When next Emmie caught sight of him, he was waltzing with a vivacious blonde girl in a scintillating Lurex dress, and Emmie herself was forced to give her entire attention to getting through three repeats of the Blue Danube with a pimply-faced youth in rubber-soled shoes who plunged her hand up and down like the handle of a well-pump and trod all over her toes as he surged forward on every downbeat with a good deal more enthusiasm than subtlety.

The night dragged on. Interminably. Would it never end? she asked herself desperately.

There was no sign of Sue and Kevin anywhere in the hall, and now she couldn't even see Ridd around, either. Maybe they had all gone home. Maybe they had *dumped* her. Maybe they had even forgotten that she had come with them at all!

She giggled, weakly, too weary to even become alarmed at the thought of such abandonment, or to worry as to how on earth she'd get home. Serve her right if they'd left her! Maybe she had convinced them that she was having a whale of a time, with all this bright, incessant chatter, this brittle laughter that came bubbling up so easily into her throat!

Emmie Montfort—the life and soul of the party!

When a couple of rusty fiddles and the accordion struck up the National Anthem she stood at attention dutifully along with the rest, and then made her way thankfully towards the exit.

The night air was warm, but still cooler than inside the hall. Smoke-free, too. She gulped it in as she stood, undecided as to what to do next.

'Here she is.' Kevin's voice. 'Where in heaven's name did you get to?'

'I might ask the same of you,' she retaliated in a meaning whisper, as she sank gratefully into the softness of the leather upholstery in the back of Ridd's saloon. 'How did it go?' she asked, taking advantage of the fact that Ridd himself was walking around the front of the vehicle with Susan to the passenger side.

'I'll tell you later,' he whispered back, but he reached across and gave her hand a quite uncharacteristic squeeze that certainly did seem to have a measure of triumph about it.

In the light from the dash, Susan's face appeared softly tranquil and composed as usual, Ridd's dark and enigmatic. Impossible to tell how the evening had turned out. She would just have to control her curiosity until an opportunity presented itself for Kevin to enlighten her.

She hadn't long to wait.

On the journey home she dozed fitfully, lulled by the hum of the engine and the soft swish of tyres in the dust, and it seemed no time at all before they were pulling up outside her own small white weatherboard abode, and she was being shaken gently into wakefulness.

'I'll see you inside, Emmie.'

Kevin took her arm and guided her up the new gravel path. The stones glimmered dimly in the moonlight, and the gravel made a satisfying, scrunchy sound beneath their feet.

'We'd better go around the back. The bell might waken Mrs. Bexley.'

In the lean-to at the rear, Emmie fumbled for the light switch, turned to her escort.

'Thanks, Kev, I'll be fine now. You go back.'

'I will in a minute." He hesitated, and then he stepped forward and took her hands. 'Darling Emmie, I want to thank you for what you did tonight,' he said in a husky, vibrant voice.

'I did nothing at all, except dance around all evening in a most exhausting manner.'

'You did! You know what I'm talking about, and it has nothing to do with dancing. No, Emmie, I owe you a debt that I'll never be able to repay, for forcing me into some sort of action tonight. I needed someone to do what you did, say what you said. I don't blame you, or Sue, for thinking me spineless, I really don't.' ·

'Oh, Kev! I've never thought you that, and you know it.'

'Well, Sue did. Yes, she did, and she was quite right, of course. I was wrapped up in myself and my own stupid introspection, not thinking of her at all. Fearful of getting hurt, rebuffed, snubbed, or whatever you like to call it. And so I did nothing. My will seemed to be frozen into non-existence, and I'd brainwashed myself into thinking I was a complete failure. Damn it all, a man's supposed to have some guts, some initiative, and I had none, did nothing that was as positive as either of those two things. And then you made me see it, Emmie. You forced me to do something physical about it, and the mental processes got going again too. All of a sudden I could see what a waste of emotion it all was, how futile, fruitless. I said to myself as I walked across the floor towards her, Darn it all, I said, the girl's right, it's at least better to be a *positive* failure than a negative one!'

'And——?'

'You were right about the other too, Emm. Susan does still feel something. We both knew it, as soon as we touched each other—the old magic is still there, the old chemistry, it still works. It will just take time, a little time, that's all, to make her completely certain about it. But I'll get a kick out of wooing her all over again, and I have a feeling that it's all going to end up the way we both want it.'

'Kevin, I'm so—so glad.' Emmie's voice was soft. Words seemed quite inadequate to show the true joy and relief she felt for himself and Sue.

'It's all thanks to you, Emmie.'

'No, Kev.'

'Yes, Emmie.' He took her face in his hands and kissed her gently. 'Do you know that you're the most wonderful girl, Emmie my darling? You've made me very, very happy.'

'Things will be different from now on.'

'Not between *us*, they won't. We understand each other, don't we? You understand just what I've been saying?'

'Yes, Kev, I do, and it makes me very, very happy too,' she breathed fervently. 'I was beginning to feel quite worried that I was pushing you into something that you didn't want. I felt quite miserable earlier, but now you've reassured me.'

There was a sound from the shadow of the back step.

'Well, it's nice to know that everyone is so happy,' drawled Ridd Fenton deeply, 'but if you don't mind cutting out any further touching farewells just now, Kev, we'll all get home. Might I remind you that we share the same transport, and you do happen to be taking the devil of a time?'

'Oh, sure, Ridd. Sorry.' Kevin chucked her under the chin in a triumphantly playful way. ' 'Night, Emm. Sleep well.'

He was whistling softly as he followed that other taller figure that was already taking the new gravel pathway in crunching strides.

CHAPTER EIGHT

EMMIE did not sleep well, in spite of Kevin's good wishes that she might. She checked that the children were sound, reassured herself that Mrs. Bexley's even breathing came from the stretcher which she had rigged up beside Daisy's, and then tiptoed quietly to her own room.

She could not have said what it was that kept her awake. A vague sense of loss, an elusive regret for something she couldn't even name or recognise. She tossed irritably, and then, when morning came, sank into a deep sleep, and it was almost ten o'clock before she woke.

She had just showered and eaten a meagre and unenthusiastic breakfast when Ridd turned up to collect Mrs. Bexley again. Emmie could see her with the children on the grass outside the kitchen window.

'I'll be with you presently, Mrs. B.,' she heard Ridd call, and then his brisk steps came nearer, up the side of the house. An instant later he was there beside her, flinging his hat on the dresser and saying without preamble,

'Where can we be alone? I want to speak to you.'

Emmie blinked.

'We *are* alone,' she pointed out feebly, wondering what could have caused that thunderous calm in Ridd's level grey eyes, a lull-before-the-storm sort of calm that might have made her quake with apprehension if he'd given her time. He didn't.

'In here will do.' He pushed her into the store-room, shut the door, and came across to her with a certain measure of deliberation. 'Now, Emily. Perhaps you'll be good enough to tell me just what you think you're playing at?'

He sounded—well, *fierce*. His brows were coming together into one of those brooding scowls, and his mouth was taut and forbidding.

Emmie blinked again, this time with genuine puzzlement. 'Playing at? Whatever do you mean?'

'You know perfectly well what I mean!'

'I don't, I'm sorry to say, Ridd. If I had the least notion of what you're getting at, I'd answer, but I haven't. Would you mind explaining what's behind that extraordinary question?'

'The explanation is for you to make. And I've no intention of spelling out the whole unsavoury business in words of one syllable for your edification. We both know what I'm talking about when I simply say it's your attitude to Kevin Condor that concerns me.'

'I still don't understand.'

'I'm sure you do.'

'I don't, Ridd. Honestly. I mean——' She hesitated, fumbling for the right words. 'I like Kevin very much.'

'Are you in *love* with him?' How strangely he was conducting this surprising conversation! How oddly and intently he was watching her! 'Enough to *marry* him?' insisted Ridd quietly.

'No, of course not. I've just said I *liked* him, haven't I? There's no question of my ever wanting to marry Kevin.' She hesitated, added frostily, 'It seems to me an odd thing for you to come here at ten in the morning to find out, but I hope you're satisfied. And now, Ridd, may I go?'

He blocked her path effectively by the simplest of means. His fingers were biting into her arms as they stopped her progress past him to the door. His khaki-shirted chest was as effective a barrier as any brick wall.

'No, you may not,' he said in clipped accents, and Emmie could see that there was a dangerous glitter in his eyes, a pallor about his mouth that told her the lull was almost over. The storm could break at any time, by the look of things, and for the life of her she couldn't see what it was she had said or done to provoke it.

'Is that all you have to say on the matter?' he persisted,

and there was a twist almost of disgust to his lips now.

'Only that I wish you would mind your own business, and let me mind mine,' she retorted, with cold dignity and a meaning glance at the brown, square-tipped fingers still clamping her arms.

'My God, but you're a cool one!' A savage shake jerked her head back, brought her wide, astonished eyes to his grim face. 'You'd better get this straight, Emily. Lay off Kevin, do you hear?'

'Are you by any chance suggesting——'

'Not suggesting. It's an ultimatum,' he told her crushingly. 'Leave him alone. If I ever catch you kissing Kevin Condor again after what you've just admitted, by heaven I'll——'

'Don't you think that's up to Kevin?' She was becoming angry herself now. Her face was flaming with a sudden rush of pure annoyance at the nerve of him, interfering, dictating, commanding, when he couldn't possibly know——

'It's more up to *you*,' he barked. 'I don't blame Kev at all. The man's in a state of emotional shock, has been ever since he came back to Koolonga, and I dare say you're a convincing little performer when you get started. I was nursing him along nicely until *you* arrived on the scene. For all I know you might be going through some particular form of hell yourself, Emily—rebounds can be damn painful things, as we once agreed—but don't go involving Kevin. Don't go relieving your frustrated emotions on him, do you hear? He's in a confused state, and he's not fit to cope with another let-down, which is what he's obviously headed for if you don't stop playing around with him!'

'How dare you! I'll play around with whom I please,' she heard herself say loftily. His face was blurred in angry mists that swam before her eyes.

'You won't. Not with Kevin.'

'I will! With whom I *please*!' Her voice rose.

'You'll pick someone your own weight, Emily, do you hear? You'll choose someone who's got your measure, not an emotional wreck like Kev. You'll pick someone who *knows* your intentions are nil, who *knows* that you're merely salving your female pride after some scorching affair that obviously went stale on you, and——'

'That's unforgivable!'

'And if it's kisses you want'—Ridd's voice was harsh—'you can get them any time, free, frivolous, no strings attached. In fact, here's one to be going on with, you brazen little minx!'

His arms went around her, bringing her against him. His lips came down with a possessive force that carried Emmie off on a tide of pain and humiliation.

It was the cruellest of kisses. Emmie had had no idea that a kiss could be such a thing—dominating, seeking, penetrating, relentless. Her senses swam. Her head was hard against his encircling arm, her hands held fistfuls of his shirt to save herself from falling.

Her frantic struggles became feeble, until she lay like a rag doll against him, praying that she could somehow manage to remain on her feet.

And then it all stopped as suddenly as it had begun. Abruptly. One moment she was pushing with a final ineffectual futility, and the next Ridd was actually putting her away from him and just sort of *standing* there, the blaze in his eyes giving way to the oddest intermingling of perplexity, bafflement, compunction.

Emmie put the back of her hand to her bruised mouth and regarded him with wide, terrified eyes. She was shaking all over. Even when Ridd stepped forward mechanically and helped her to a chair, she didn't think her limbs might even make the short distance involved.

'I'm sorry, Emily. Very sorry.' The deep voice beside her was gruff. Formal. 'Are you all right?'

She nodded numbly. 'I don't understand.'

Those few protesting words were all she could manage.

'Neither do I.' He sounded unbelievably grim. 'Not nearly as well as I thought I did five minutes ago. Two and two don't appear to make four this time.' A pause. 'Are you sure you're O.K., Emily?' Ridd asked again, and this time there was no doubting the solicitous regret in him that almost reached out and enfolded her. She couldn't bear it.

'Please go.' Her lips were stiff.

'Would you like me to get you something? A drink of water? Some tea?'

'Please go.' It was all she seemed able to say. 'Please go.'

She watched him dumbly as he walked across and opened the door, and when he went out she sat on for quite a long time without even moving, in just the same position as she had been when he put her there, her shoulders hunched, her arms folded about herself as if to protect herself against her own agony of mind.

Emmie saw little of him after that.

It was Kevin who came, still, to work the electric light plant, and Kevin who also came to collect any stores. Some times in the early mornings she still heard the thud of an axe as it bit into the logs in her woodshed, and there were the same neatly cut blocks piled up as usual, but if the woodcutter was Ridd, he was always gone before she herself got up to waken the children, and if he rode by on horseback or drove past in the jeep, she found herself automatically shrinking away from the windows, taking care to remain out of sight.

It was a measure of compensation that her friendship with Sue Wensley blossomed into a comfortable companionship that was everything Emmie could have wished and longed for.

The other girl often rode over during the remainder of the holidays, and when school reopened she sometimes came at week-ends for a while, chatted amicably, played with the children, helped with whatever activity happened to be on hand at the time. Their relationship had none of the hard edges and prickly moments that Emmie had formerly found so disconcerting, and Susan herself seemed to have acquired a new dimension of inner happiness that gave her an impulsive charm, a glow, a *joie de vivre* that had not been there before. She was like a sister to Emmie. More like a sister, indeed, than either Lissa or Sharon had ever been!

The red paint arrived in due course, and Emmie got to work on the roof. Kevin left a ladder with her, and did a little in his spare time, and even Susan put on a dab or two, although she said it was much too hot and unpleasant up there for long. The heat went right through the soles of one's sandshoes. The sun beat down ruthlessly, and the rays were thrown back on to one's face from the corrugated iron sheets. The colour was a pretty one, though. A subtle, dull brick shade that contrasted well with the white weather-board and the drab grey-green of the eucalypts in the background. The paint dried almost as rapidly as one applied it, and Emmie had given it the required two coats well before the rain began.

For the last few days the clouds seemed to have been gathering and dispersing as if they couldn't make up their minds.

Emmie watched them grumbling around the horizon for a long time before they finally decided to pack together in a heavy grey column and roll slowly towards Koolonga. Then the day became dark and sombre, thunder growled in the distance, and suddenly the heavens seemed to part, and rain pelted down in heavy, impenetrable sheets. It rained steadily for the whole of the rest of the day, and when darkness fell the tattoo of it was still hammering incessantly on the roof.

It was pleasant to be shut in, warm and comfortable and dry, with her little family tucked up cosily, while outside the wind got up to a howling force that lashed the gumtrees into a wailing whine, and drove the raindrops harder, harder, until the din was deafening—pleasant, that is, until she was making her final routine peep before retiring, and saw that Daisy's bed was empty.

Emmie stared, disbelieving for a moment. Then she checked the bathroom; the veranda where the boys were sound on their cross-legged stretchers; the kitchen; the other room; everywhere. Even (stupidly) in wardrobes, under the beds themselves. Nowhere a sign of Daisy.

Emmie bit her lip, took a grip on herself. Then she went out to the veranda, lifted the mosquito-nets, shook the boys gently.

'Jim? Jim, have you seen Daisy?'

'What? Daisy? No.' He was impossibly sleepy. Emmie couldn't get any sense out of him. She tugged at Morris instead.

'Morrie? Do wake up! Do you know where Daisy is?'

'Isn't she in bed?' Morris sat up, tousled, his eyes widening.

'No, she doesn't seem to be.' Seeing his eyes grow even wider, she pushed him down on the pillow again, patted his sleepy head with a calmness she was far from feeling. 'Never mind, Morrie. Go back to sleep, and don't worry. I—I haven't even looked around the house yet.'

No sense in alarming them when they obviously couldn't assist her.

'The bathroom,' mumbled Morris helpfully, his eyes closed again already.

'Yes, of course. How silly of me! Goodnight, darling.'

' 'Night, Emmie.'

Emmie went back and rechecked the child's room. It stared at her reproachfully, empty of everything but the pretty pale walls, the chintz flower patterns on the curtains. The bedclothes were scarcely rumpled.

The drumming from above her head was drumming panic into Emmie's mind as well, although she tried to resist. She grabbed a torch and ran out into the downpour, shone the light into one shed after another, calling as she did so. Her cries were drowned in the deluge, snatched away on the wind.

'Daisy? Daisy, where are you?'

Emmie was running again. Her throat was hoarse with shouting.

What was she to do? What if she couldn't find her? What

if she had run away? What if Emmie hadn't made her happy here, after all? Just say she'd been secretly miserable all this time, miserable enough to want to leave—although one couldn't believe it of the bubbling, mercurial, irrepressible little Daisy—where would she go, a small, dusky, black-frizzed orphan, with no home, no people?

No people? But she had, hadn't she? Or at least, one half of her had people. Those nebulous dark people, who would recognise their kinship if she sought shelter from them in their close-knit society. The nomadic aborigines that wandered still in the innermost interior of this vast continent, living off the land as they went from place to place, digging for yams, scraping the soaks for water, following the seasons, spearing fish and kangaroos and lizards, prying the witchetty grubs from under the bark to cook and cool them before they ate the cold creamy-rich delicacies with a relish that maybe even Daisy might share if she had to.

Had Daisy perhaps gone walkabout? Would some hidden sense urge her on, tell her where to go to find those people of hers? There had always been something a little bit fey about her, an ancient wisdom and a self-reliance quite startling in one so young. She could 'frighten' easily, too, though. Very easily. That, too, was part of the legacy of her imaginative, superstitious race. Surely she'd be frightened now, out here in this tearing wind, this lashing wet. Emmie certainly was! There were debil-debils aplenty let loose tonight!

'Daisy? Daisy?'

What *was* she to do?

Emmie stood still, with the raindrops pounding on her bare, soaked head, and tried to collect herself.

Ridd? No, she couldn't tell him. He, of all people, mustn't hear. 'If you default with the children'—his words rattled the chains of hysteria that had already shackled her brain. She fled again down the track, stumbling into ruts and splashing through puddles, her mind made up.

She'd have to go to the kiosk near the old Post Office. She could phone Susan from there. It was almost half-way to the school, but at least it would save her the extra couple of miles on a night such as this. Perhaps Daisy might even be with Susan right now. She liked her teacher, liked the school. Maybe she had forgotten something at the schoolhouse, and had slipped back stealthily in the dark, in spite of the rain. What could be so important to her, though? Or was she truly a child of the open, with her ancestors' hardiness? Perhaps the weather hadn't daunted her after all. Maybe the old superstitions had been laid by her environment, and devil-spirits no longer held sway for Daisy.

When she reached the phone box, Emmie wrenched open the door, staggered in and slammed it again. Inside, she wound the handle, giving the code ring of shorts and longs that made up Susan's number on the party line to which the instrument was connected.

It was answered almost immediately.

The other girl listened attentively as Emmie babbled out her message.

'Hold on, Emmie, till I think. Are you quite certain you've looked everywhere?'

'*Everywhere.*' Emmie was despairing.

'Well, don't panic.' Susan's tone was comforting. 'I want you to do something, Emmie. Stay right where you are, in the phone box, will you?'

'Oh, Sue! You mean you'll come?'

'Of course I'll come. We'll organise something. You stay there.'

'Sue, bless you for that! I do appreciate it. I knew I could count on you.'

'Keep your chin up, Emmie. I'm sure she'll be around somewhere, the little rascal.'

The receiver went down, and the line went dead.

Emmie stayed there in the box for what seemed an incalculable time. She leaned against the wall and recovered her breath while a pool of water gathered at her feet as it streamed off her person on to the floor.

Finally impatience drove her out into the storm again.

She'd keep to the track, and Sue could pick her up. If she called as she went, there was just a chance that Daisy might hear her, wherever she was. There was the faintest possibility of locating her before Sue turned up, in which case there would be laughter and tears and recriminations all round!

She hadn't even made a mile of it when she was picked out in the car's headlights. Emmie stood at the side of the road and waited. If the rain hadn't been coursing down her face and blurring her vision she might have known that it was Ridd and not Susan who was at the wheel of that car, but he had opened the passenger door, leaned over and dragged her in before she could utter a word.

'Oh! It's—you!'

'As you see.' He shot her a quick, comprehensive glance. 'Take it easy, Emily. Just tell me where you've looked, and if you can think of any reason for Daisy to disappear like this?'

There was something steadying about his solid form beside her, and his formal, practical manner. She sat back against the cushioned upholstery, a small, sodden, distraught figure, shook her head miserably.

'I've looked everywhere. *Everywhere.* And I can't think why she'd want to do it, unless——' She clasped her hands together, twisted them. Turned to face the granite profile. Ridd was staring ahead in concentration as the wipers cleared the windscreen and the rain obscured his vision again almost immediately. The car was going fast, slithering in the sea of mud that had once been the road.

'I—I had to rebuke her this morning,' she confessed with anguish. 'Oh, it was just a trifle, nothing serious. She took it all right, or at least I thought she did, only now I keep asking myself if—if——'

'All kids need a firm hand now and again. It won't be that. Have you asked the boys?'

'I didn't want to go into it too deeply. It seemed they didn't know anything, although they were very sleepy when I questioned them. I knew I'd have to go out, so I didn't dare wake them up too much. There was no one to leave them with.'

'I told Susan to stay where she was, just in case Daisy might have been on her way there. It's not likely, though. My guess is that there's a simple explanation, and that she's quite near at hand. It's a hell of a night for anyone to go out into.'

Emmie winced, thinking of Daisy. She was frozen herself by now. Chilled to the marrow, in fact. Numb. Weary.

'That's what I keep thinking, too. She'll be s-soaked, and maybe frightened. She's only *little*.'

He didn't answer that. She saw his mouth compress itself in the dim light, and he drove in silence, without slackening speed, until he swung the car off the main road and pulled up outside the store.

'I'll see those boys first of all.' He followed her inside, went straight to the sleep-out and flung back the mosquito nets. 'Wake up, mates! It's Ridd!' He pulled and pummelled them awake with none of Emmie's gentleness. 'Now then. A dollar to the one who hits it first. Where's Daisy, and why has she run away?'

Emmie waited nearby, listening rather hopelessly to the patient catechism that was going on, and this time it was on to her own veranda floorboards that the rainwater was dripping from her clothes.

Ridd's voice went on and on, sifting information, getting his answers systematically. No quarrels today? Sure about that? What did you all do, then? Where did you go when you came back from school? No, tell me exactly. Everything you can think of. Each little thing.

It had turned into a game, for the boys at least. They vied for his attention, prompting each other in the cause of accuracy.

'No, you didn't. That was *before*.'

'No, after.'

'No, before, Morrie. It was after that that Bingo chased Quinty up the tree. Daisy was pretty angry about *that*.'

'Angry?' Ridd was all attention.

'Quinty's going to have kittens,' Jim explained. 'At least, we *think* she is. We think she was looking for a place to have them, see, and Bingo kept following her around and chasing her out of the sheds. They don't like each other much.'

'He's only a pup, that's what I told Daisy. He doesn't really mean it. He's got to learn. I told her that, but she belted him because he wouldn't let Quinty find a place in peace. In the end I tied him up.'

'And what did Quinty do then, Morrie?'

'Oh, she was still up the tree. We waited around for ages, but she wouldn't come down. She was still there even after tea. And then, later, she came down and ran away. She went away up the railway line, and over near the signal-box.'

Ridd's eyes sought Emmie's. 'Did you look at the station, Emmie?'

'No, I didn't. I—I hunted everywhere here, through the house itself, and then through all the sheds and outbuildings. And then I w-went to ring Susan. It was the only thing I could think of to do. I never thought of the railway station.'

She was shivering by now, uncontrollably.

'I'll look,' he said evenly, and turned to the boys. 'Simmer down, you chaps. If this hunch pays off, it's a dollar for each of you, *if* you go to sleep and don't bother Emily.' He took her arm. 'Go and have a hot bath and give yourself a good rub down with the towel. Dry your hair afterwards, will you?'

'I'm coming.'

'No, leave it with me, and do as I say. The boys are awake now, in any case.'

'Please, Ridd. I'll wait till you come back—for the bath, I mean.' Her eyes were tortured. 'Do you really think you'll find her?'

'Yes, I'll find her.' He made it sound such a certainty that Emmie almost felt able to believe him.

163

She was unsurprised when he came up the path not long afterwards with Daisy in his arms, a small oilskin bundle enclosed in his big black waterproof riding-cape. As he shouldered his way through the door and walked towards Daisy's bedroom, Emmie could see that his own hair was thoroughly wet now, too, but he still wore the military-looking raincoat he had had on from the start. The oilskin was obviously a spare.

Beneath it, Daisy was quite dry. There wasn't a drop of rain on her bright candy-striped pyjamas as he slipped her into bed, and said softly to Emmie,

'She's fine. She was underneath the platform itself, with her coat and gumboots beside her. It's quite weatherproof under there. Quinty picked a good spot to have her kittens. She's got five.'

'Two blacks, a grey, and—two—that are sort of—brindle,' murmured Daisy through shut eyes. 'We mustn't let Bingo get them.'

'We won't,' Emmie whispered. 'Go to sleep again, Daisy.'

'I'll just tell the boys to keep him tied up in the morning, and then I'll get home. I'll see about getting a phone connected, too, Emily, after this. It only means taking on the poles, an extention of the existing line.'

Ridd walked out on to the veranda. Afterwards Emmie followed him to the door.

'Thank you,' she said. There wasn't anything much else she *could* say, was there? She felt incredibly foolish not to have thought of looking up at the station before bothering Susan.

'Get into that bath now,' he instructed abruptly.

'Yes, I will.' She watched him lift his collar against the pelting rain as he prepared to leave. 'R-Ridd?'

'Yes?'

It was difficult to speak, because her teeth were chattering so violently. She really *did* need that hot bath badly!

'R-Ridd, you'll be g-g-glad of the r-rain, w-won't you? It will be g-good for your sh-sh-sheep, won't it? You won't h-have to c-cut s-s-s-scrub for a w-while.'

He turned, hunched into his upturned collar, his face unreadable. He took so long to reply that she almost wondered if, in the end, he hadn't been going to say something altogether different to what he *did* say.

'That's right, Emily,' he said to her, in a surprised sort of way, almost as if she had told him something he didn't already know himself.

And then he disappeared into the darkness of the storm, and Emmie went to light the chip heater and wait for the water to get hot.

Perhaps it was that final interval of sitting about in her dressing-gown, still cold and clammy from her wetting, while the geyser got slowly to work eating up the kindlers she had fed it, that was responsible for the chill she seemed to have caught.

It wasn't much, she told herself.

In fact, it had only come on two days later. The following morning she had felt quite normal, and thank goodness the children appeared to have taken the episode in their stride. They were delighted with the kittens, and Emmie, kneeling on the gravel with them and peering under the sloping railway platform, marvelled at the soft sweetness of the small furry things that kneaded at Quinty's soft fur blindly, mewing piercingly.

The cat had retreated to the farthermost point of the cavity, where the gap between ceiling and ground was at its narrowest. The children, even crawling on their tummies, could not get within touching distance, and certainly Bingo's fat, roly-poly body might have got wedged, too, but Emmie had decided not to risk any further disasters. Bingo would be tied up when he wasn't actually in the house with her there to keep an eye on him, or when the children had arrived home from school and could give him their proper attention.

He sat on his haunches in a smart new collar and chain which the store stock had obligingly provided, looking guilty and smug at the same time. Emmie took pity on him, went back into the kitchen and produced a beef-bone for him to chew and worry over to relieve his boredom until the children reappeared, ignored the soreness in her throat and the tension behind her eyes.

A cold. And who'd be surprised, after such a drenching?

Well, maybe not exactly a cold, she corrected herself a couple of days later still. More like a sort of 'flu. Her head was aching, and there was a leaden weight attached to each of her limbs. She dragged around in the morning for a bit, and in the afternoon lay down on her bed, dozing fitfully until nearer the time of the children's return, when she heaved herself up reluctantly to get the tea.

'Don't say anything to Susan, will you?' she bade them croakily. 'It's just a touch of 'flu. This is its worst day. I'll be better tomorrow.'

She wasn't, though. In fact she wondered quite how she got through the next day, and the next. There was a rasping pain inside her ribs that just wouldn't go away, and every breath was becoming an agony. She waved the children off in her dressing-gown and crept back to bed, taking some more aspirin with her as she went, so that she would not have to get up again.

She huddled under the bedclothes, shivering violently, praying that nothing would disturb her ever again, and that she wouldn't find it necessary to cough. She asked herself if there was anything further she could do, in the name of common sense, to get herself better, but she couldn't concentrate on the problem for long. Her head was pounding too desperately, and she found she had enough to think about, merely in getting her breath.

The walls closed in as she lay there, and the ceiling hovered just above her. It was claustrophobic. Lonely. She longed unreasonably for the reassuring sound of the children's voices, bringing cheer to the stillness, even if it did mean somehow getting up again.

Would they be home soon? She didn't know. She couldn't even seem to summon the necessary energy to lean over to the bedside table to turn the clock face nearer so that she could see what the hands were saying. She couldn't even be bothered to take any more of that aspirin, either, that was there, *somewhere* there, beside the clock.

There were footsteps now. They scrunched up the gravel pathway and into Emmie's consciousness.

The children. Lots of steps. Big, heavy, elephantine steps. Those clowning children! Some sort of game. Elephants today. One of those childish flights of fancy to which they sometimes devoted themselves.

Even the scrunch of the elephant-steps reverberated. It irritated, annoyed. She must get up when the steps came right inside. Get up and get the tea. She'd wait till they came right in, though. She'd wait till the last possible minute, because she wasn't too sure that she could bring herself to get up at all!

The steps had congregated somewhere near the back of the lean-to. Now they stopped altogether.

'Emily?'

Oh lord! It was Ridd Fenton's voice, not the children at all! The shock of it brought her right back to her senses.

'Yes?' She meant to sound brisk and businesslike, but her voice was disappointing.

'I've got the men here, to install the telephone. Do you want it in the hall, or the main store? Which?'

The *telephone*! She thought fast.

'The store,' she shouted, only it wasn't much of a shout.

'The what?'

'The—store.'

She couldn't say it again, not even once more. It had taken too much energy to speak already. There was that knife in her ribs again, and she felt a band of sweat breaking on her forehead with the effort of it all.

She lay back, sighing.

'Emily, where *are* you?'

167

Emmie lay back and closed her eyes. It seemed the simplest way out of things. Just close your eyes and pretend you weren't there. Pretend that Ridd wasn't there either.

'Emily?' Steps again. The bedroom door. 'Emily?'

Ridd was there, beside her now. She hadn't actually opened her eyes, but she knew it all the same. She opened them now, to confirm the situation. Yes, there he was, standing there with his hat in one hand, bending over her.

'Emily?' Ridd's voice was slow and careful. He was a careful sort of man, Ridd Fenton. Deliberate. Controlled. Always master of the situation. No, not always, not *quite* always, not when he got suddenly, blazingly angry and kissed so ruthlessly, so cruelly, so terribly. She preferred him this way, really. Careful, controlled, slow and unalarming.

His hand was already searching for her pulse, but even that was a slow, precise, careful gesture. 'How long have you been like this?'

He made it sound important, as if he expected an answer. Emmie thought a moment.

'A few days. I'm better.'

It was a wearying business, this talking. A fresh dew broke out on her forehead.

'Why are you propped up like that, Emily?'

'More—comfortable,' she gasped, and closed her eyes again in disgust. What a stupid question! Not up to the usual Riddley Fenton standard at all!

'What are you doing?' she managed to ask hoarsely, her eyes flying open again as she felt the blankets being pulled from the corners of the bed and a hand sliding purposefully behind her shoulders.

'I'm taking you home.' Ridd's tone was curt.

'Home?'

'Koolonga. Lie still, Emily.'

'The—telephone?'

'They'll carry on.'

'In—the store?'

'In the hall. More central.'

She gave up after that. Ridd would always have the last word, anyway, and she couldn't be bothered to argue, not even about an important and permanent item such as a telephone.

Emmie wasn't too sure of anything very definitely after that.

She remembered Ridd wrapping the blankets around her and taking her out, past the telephone men who stared curiously as he carried her past them through the hall. Then she was in bed again, and Ridd and Kevin were there. They hovered about on the other side of the room, speaking in low tones, and every now and then one of them would step out on to the veranda and look through the gauze.

'No sign?'

'Not yet. He shouldn't be long now.'

They were waiting for someone. The doctor, of course. Ridd would always do the sensible thing. She closed her eyes against the sensible, controlled Riddley Fenton. The Master of the Situation.

'I've given her a fairly massive dose. I don't want to move her in her present distressed condition.'

'How long before it will work?'

'It'll start to take effect straight away, or should do. You needn't expect to see much of a change before twenty-four hours, though. She'll get some rest in the meantime. Can you handle one of these things?'

'When I have to.'

'Give her another jab in twelve hours, then. I'll leave it with you.'

They were talking above her, just as if she wasn't there at all.

'And then——?'

'Then carry on with the tablets. If there's not a marked improvement by then, let me know, Ridd, and we'll admit her, but she's a bit low for the journey just now.' A pause. 'It'd be a guide if I knew any past medical history. You don't——?'

'Strong as a horse,' whispered Emmie, but nobody even caught the thin thread of sound.

'I know nothing,' said Ridd Fenton abruptly.

'Hmm. Pity. Never mind, we'll have to play it by ear. Mrs. Bexley has nursing experience?'

'She's capable. If you say not to move her——'

'I'd prefer not, for various reasons.'

'We'll do it this way, then.'

The voices died away.

CHAPTER NINE

Mrs. Bexley was sitting in a cane chair by the bed. She had on a white apron and she was working busily at a piece of knitting. A strong face, Mrs. Bexley's. A good woman. Capable, like Ridd had said. A good strong honest face. Emmie felt a twinge of shame for having deceived her.

'I'm sorry, Mrs. Bexley.'

'What's that, dear?' The housekeeper put down the piece of knitting, and leaned forward.

'I've always—meant—to say it. About—the tomatoes——'

'Don't talk, Emmie. Save your breath for breathing with,' said Mrs. Bexley practically, in her eminently sensible way.

Emmie turned her head on the pillow irritably.

'You haven't followed. I—want—to apologise, Mrs. Bexley.'

'What was that, Emmie?' Mrs Bexley had to lean forward all over again.

'I never returned the bacon—I meant to——'

'Ssh!'

'And a whole—*basket*—of tomatoes. You—didn't know, did you? *Did* you, Mrs. Bexley?'

'Know what, Emmie?' Mrs. Bexley got up. Her face hovered.

'Kevin offered me—some—cheeses, too. But they were—Ridd's—so I couldn't. I wouldn't have—taken—anything—from Ridd. You *do* see, Mrs. Bexley?'

But Mrs. Bexley couldn't answer, because she wasn't there any more. It was Ridd's face that hovered now. Very near where Mrs. Bexley's had been. Emmie felt his fingers smoothing her damp hair back from her forehead.

'What makes you think I'd have minded, Emily?' he was

asking gently. 'What cheeses?'

'*I* minded.'

'Don't talk any more, Emily. Go to sleep.'

'The—Master—of—the—Situation.'

'What's that?' Ridd bent over her.

'The Master—of—the—Situation.'

'That's right,' said Kevin cheerfully, from the chair where Ridd had been sitting. 'Everything's hunky-dory now, thanks to you, Emm. Get some shut-eye, will you, old girl? I'm *sleepy*.'

'I've been thinking, Kev——'

'Mm?'

'Thinking—things—over——'

'What's that, Emily?'

'I've been—thinking. It might all—have been—quite different—thinking *back*, you know—different if——'

'If what?'

'If you—hadn't—kissed me——'

But it was Ridd who was there again, not Kevin at all.

Ridd looked quite startled. He was pale underneath his heavy tan, and there was a stubble of beard on his chin and cheeks. He looked like a gaunt, grim, sallow-faced pirate.

'Try to forget it,' said the pirate softly. 'Just for a while. Don't think about it just now.'

'Don't—*you*—ever think——?'

'I'm going to give you an injection, Emily,' said the pirate sternly. 'You'll hardly feel a thing, I promise.'

And he carried her off to his pirate ship, and the sea lapped gently against the edges of the boat. She was lulled to sleep in the swaying trough of the ocean.

'Are you feeling better, Emily?'

Ridd smiled a little, felt her forehead with the palm of his hand.

'Much better, thank you. Much, much better. What's the time?'

'About four o'clock.'

'Morning?'

172

'No, afternoon. It's daylight out there beyond the curtains.'

'Thursday?'

'No, Friday. Would you like a cup of tea?'

'I can think of nothing I'd like more at this moment, if it wouldn't be a nuisance?'

He got up stiffly from the cane chair beside her.

'I'll get Mrs. Bexley to bring you one,' Ridd Fenton said heavily. 'I'm going to go and have a shave.' He passed his hand over his stubbled chin and went away.

Emmie did not see Ridd again after that, for days and days and days. She slept, woke, slept, gazed incuriously around the room, spoke to the doctor quite lucidly when he came back again, drank Mrs. Bexley's endless cups of tea, ate boiled eggs and lightly buttered toast—sometimes with relish, sometimes without—had several short, uninformative, cheering chats with Kevin, slept, woke, slept some more.

Finally she asked, listlessly, of Mrs. Bexley,

'Where's Ridd?'

'Ridd? He's away, my dear.' The housekeeper plumped the pillows with efficient briskness and glanced sharply at Emmie's drawn, pale, upraised face. 'Why do you ask?'

Emmie shrugged. 'I'd like to go home soon. I'm feeling better, and I want to get back to the store.'

'You aren't strong enough yet, Emmie. Besides, Ridd wouldn't like it.'

'No, that's why I asked. I don't want to go off behind his back again. He's been very kind, allowing me to come here, getting the doctor, looking after me. You *all* have.'

'He'd have done the same for anybody. Don't fret.'

'What about the children? *They'll* be fretting.'

'No, they won't. They're back with Susan in the meantime. Ridd thought it would be too noisy for you, having them here. You were quite ill for a while, you know.'

'Just a chill. Nothing like that has ever happened to me before. I suppose I was a bit careless when Daisy went missing. I was almost out of my mind, but even so, I should have had the presence of mind to at least put on a coat. Ridd had *two*, one on, and one spare.'

'That's Ridd. He's always organised,' Mrs. Bexley smiled. 'He even took Quinty and her kittens over to the school-house with the children, so they wouldn't mind leaving the store all over again.'

'And Bingo?'

'He's here, at Koolonga. He might keep him here a while, just until those kittens are big enough to skim up a tree and out of Bingo's way. It solves the problem, and might save you worrying. Ridd's good at solving problems.'

Emmie thought about that as Mrs. Bexley whisked over the room with her duster.

'I could take Bingo back when I go. I think I could teach him to get on with the kittens.'

'Maybe,' Mrs. Bexley shrugged. 'You can't go back for at least a week yet, though.'

'A *week*?'

'That's what the doctor said, and Ridd agreed.'

'When will Ridd be back?'

Mrs. Bexley smoothed the coverlet and straightened a couple of small flower-prints on the wall. She had knocked them askew with her duster.

'He shouldn't be more than a few days, by all accounts. He went off in the plane when he was quite sure you were on the mend. Don't you remember?'

'He didn't say goodbye, or anything. He just went off to shave.'

Emmie sounded almost *hurt*. She was amazed at herself. She checked herself quickly as soon as she was aware of the fact, alarmed at that dull, sad little pang she had suffered just now. Why should he have said goodbye to her? Why should he tell *her* that he was going away? It was entirely his own affair, after all.

Emmie was sitting on the veranda when Ridd returned a few days after that. She was fully dressed. It was only the third time she had put all her clothes on, but she had been

174

walking around the verandas each morning and afternoon in her gown and pyjamas, coaxing the weakness out of her wobbly limbs.

Now she was almost completely recovered.

She had chosen the north veranda, because it escaped the afternoon sun, and it was from there that she had a clear view of the silver twin-engined aircraft as Ridd brought it in low over the homestead to settle on the airstrip where the orange wind-sock dangled limply in the still afternoon heat.

The weather had resumed its former habits. The rain might never have been, might never have fallen at all, but one knew it must have, because of the green sward that now covered the dark-soiled plains—short, lush pasture that had changed the entire aspect of the landscape, almost overnight, it seemed to Emmie.

She watched Ridd as he lifted the latch on the white wicket gate and stepped through, closed it behind him, and came striding over the lawn.

He had on a pale blue shirt against which his teak-brown face and arms looked swarthier than ever, and over his arm he carried the jacket of his tropic-weight light grey suit. The gaunt, sallow, grim-faced pirate had gone. He must have been a figment of Emmie's over-burdened imagination. The Ridd who was walking across the lawn towards her was Ridd as she knew him. Handsome, clean-shaven, confident, composed. The Master of the Situation.

He came along the side path next the gauze, disappeared around the corner and into the house. When he reappeared it was through the hall door which opened on to her own part of the veranda. The jacket had been disposed of, and he carried a tankard of beer for himself in one hand, and a tall glass of lemon barley-water in the other.

'Good afternoon, Emily. I thought you might like that.' He passed her the tall glass, chinking with ice, hitched his trousers and sat down beside her, shot her one of those quick, comprehensive, sweeping looks. 'You're better, I see. Has Mrs. Bexley been looking after you?'

'Quite splendidly, thank you, Ridd.' She found that she was suddenly, acutely shy. 'You've all been enormously kind, and I've been a trouble, I know.'

'No trouble at all, Emily,' he assured her gravely. 'We were only too glad to be able to help out.'

He stretched his legs, searched his pockets in the old, familiar way for his tobacco and papers and proceeded to roll himself a cigarette.

She waited until he had rubbed the tobacco and tilted it carefully into the oblong wafer of paper, sealed it down and placed it between his lips. Then she said,

'I can't impose on your hospitality much longer, Ridd. You've no objection to my going home soon? Kevin could drive me over.'

His lighter flared.

'Leave it a few days yet. The end of the week. I'll take you back myself.'

'Very well.' It would have been churlish to argue when they had all been so good. 'Thank you.'

'If you'll excuse me, I'll have to leave you just now. I've a fair few things to see to, after being away. It's good to see you're quite recovered, though, Emily.'

A little later she saw him, back in the khaki working clothes, walking over the lawn and out of the little wicket gate again, with the broad-brimmed hat pulled down over his face.

In the cool of the evening he reappeared.

'Would you like a short stroll around the garden, Emily?' he asked kindly. 'The fresh air might do you good, and things have come on well after the rain.'

She got to her feet, mildly surprised, but followed him along the veranda, and when he held open the gauze door and stepped aside, she went through and down the steps, and they walked around the paths and lawns and flower beds, Ridd pointing out various shrubs and trees and plants of interest.

The next evening it was Kevin who acted as her escort.

'Ridd reckoned you might like a dander around outside, Emmie. He said you seemed to enjoy it last night, and a breath of air will do you good.'

'You don't have to do that, Kev. I'm not an invalid, you know, not now. If I want to go for a walk, I can always do it myself.'

'No problem. It's my pleasure. And anyway, I want to tell you something.' At the end of the path by the cypress hedge he stopped. 'Emmie, Sue and I are going to get married.'

'Oh, Kevin! I'm so happy for you!' She turned to him, her face aglow with joy. 'When? When did you decide?'

'The other day. I've been working on it, you might say, and she's come round to my own way of thinking.' He chuckled unexpectedly. 'It wasn't as difficult as I thought it might be, getting her to agree.'

'I think it's marvellous news, anyway, Kev. You belong together, you two. I knew it from the start. This is how it should all have been in the first place, if you hadn't had to obey that call-up. It was all terribly unfortunate and badly timed. In fact it couldn't have come at a worse moment for both of you, the way you were then.'

'I know. Looking back, I can take a more detached view. I was young, high-minded, idealistic. Enthusiastic in the cause of duty and my own particular definition of patriotism. She couldn't see it my way, and we didn't discuss it sufficiently thoroughly or calmly, or we might have seen each other's points of view. She couldn't see it my way. She resented my going, saw it as a personal thing.'

'I know. She told me as much. She said you *could* have got out of going if you'd really tried.'

'That's true, I could have. But I'd have lost my self-respect, Emmie, if I'd done it that way. I'd have found it hard to live with it afterwards, no matter what Sue thought. I'd have been a fraud.'

Emmie nodded sagely. 'I don't think it was really what Sue would have wanted, either, Kev, do you know that?' she told him gently. 'You wouldn't have been quite the same man in her eyes, afterwards, although she might never have admitted it. Whatever she'd say about it now, I think she respected what you did, even if it made her so hurt and resentful that she rushed into a rather reckless marriage herself because of it. She'll love you all the more for having gone away, now, I'm sure of it.'

'You think so?' He grinned, but it was a grin of such pure happiness and contentment that she knew he was sure of it too.

'You'll have to come to the wedding, of course,' he told her, as they walked back to the house. 'You and the kids. It will just be a quiet affair. Sue's parents and sister, my own family, the Koolonga folk. Very quiet.'

'It won't be, if the kids are there,' she felt bound to point out mischievously.

'They'll have to be, all the same. Susan insists. They've been a connecting link between all of us, a bond. I reckon you came here in the first place more because of them than because of Millie's store really, didn't you, Emm?'

'That's true,' she admitted, surprised at his perception.

'Well, you can have them back on Sunday. Ridd's taking you home tomorrow, but Sue thought she'd better give you a day to yourself to settle back in again. You did leave in rather a hurry, after all.'

Yes, she had certainly left in a hurry, Kevin was right about that. She had scarcely given the place, or the way in which she had left it, much of a thought since, but now, as she and Ridd came over the ridge and down on to the plain again, she could see the little white house with its red roof and spindly sugar gums squatting on the scrub-dotted horizon.

'The telephone,' she asked suddenly. 'Where did they put it?'

'In the hall. It's central there. Easy access from the bedrooms, kitchen, and the counter itself.'

He was right, of course.

'I think you'll find everything in order,' he went on. 'Mrs.

178

Bexley and Susan have both been over since, to keep things right in your absence. When I brought Bingo away, I simply locked it up.'

Bingo yelped ecstatically from the back seat at the mention of his own name.

When they got to the front of the store, Ridd stopped the engine, got out and came around to her door. Emmie stepped out, and surveyed the place critically.

'It looks nice, the white and the red, don't you think?'

'Very nice,' agreed Ridd somewhat absently. 'You go ahead and unlock the place. I'll bring in your gear.'

He walked around to the boot with the dog at his heel, and Emmie went up her gravel path with the flagstone edging, and opened the front door.

She walked through the store, past clean dusted shelves, newly piled stock. Sue and Mrs. Bexley had been busy indeed. She'd need to thank them both for this!

In the hall stood the telephone. There was an oak seat beside it that she hadn't seen before, and a directory hung from a hook on the wall.

The key of the back door was on the inside. It had never worked very well, but she turned it in its rusty lock, opened the door, latched it into position to let the draught of air right through the building, and stepped out into the sun.

The woodshed was full of blocks and kindlers.

She shut the door again and stood still for a moment, savouring the silence, the peace, and the fact that she was home.

And then she was running. Running. Stumbling blindly over the hard, hot ground, over the small plot of grass, with steps that somehow couldn't cover the distance with adequate speed.

Even if she had got there earlier—*much* earlier—she'd have been too late. Much too late!

The choking, strangled cry she had uttered brought Ridd striding around the side of the house. When he reached her she was kneeling on the ground beside the apricot tree, trying ineffectually to put the pieces together again.

'What is it, Emily, in God's name?' Ridd's voice was harsh with alarm as he covered the last few paces at a run.

'My tree! My tree! My little tree. Just look! Oh, what can have done it?' She glanced around wildly, her eyes blank with dismay and shock.

'What was it?'

She swallowed, replied indistinctly,

'An apricot tree.'

It wasn't any more, though. Not now. Not after the depredations of whatever it was that had attacked it. There were just a few leaves, dried, withered, half buried in the trampled earth around it. A couple of twigs nearby—twigs that had once been the strong, new lateral branches of her little tree, full of promise and vigour. The main stem was crushed beyond recognition.

'What can have done it?' she was muttering distractedly. 'Oh, whatever can have *done* it?'

'It must have been the sheep.'

'The sheep? What sheep?'

'There's stock in this paddock now, Emily. The men moved them in when they picked up strength after the rain. We may or may not get a follow-up, you see, and they'll be nearer for feeding, here at the homestead block.'

She pushed the hair out of her eyes, blinked at him bewilderedly.

'What sheep?' She didn't believe him. She *couldn't*! 'I don't see any sheep.'

'Emily, it's a four-hundred-acre paddock,' Ridd pointed out, and his voice was deep and inexorable, but somehow heavy and sad as well. 'We have to net young trees if we're growing them, to protect them from the stock. The men wouldn't have known that your apricot tree was here, and neither did I.' He put a hand on her shoulder. 'We can get you another one,' he said bracingly. 'We'll soon get another one, and the men can net it properly for you.'

She shook her head blindly. 'It wouldn't be the same.'

'Why wouldn't it?'

'Not the same as this one.'

'Why not?'

'You wouldn't understand,' she told him thickly.

'Try me,' invited Ridd patiently.

'You wouldn't. You wouldn't understand at all, Ridd. You'd *never* understand. How could you?' She was babbling now, almost incoherent. 'It's not just a tree, you see—not just any tree. It was my own little tree, my own little apricot. It came here when I did, at the same time as me. We were both strange, both new, both a bit lost. It was starting a new life, just the same as I was, putting down roots in a fresh, happy place. It *liked* it here, it was beginning to *grow*. And now—and now——'

Her words trailed away, and her fingers were scrabbling in the dust, searching the trampled earth, working frantically as she gathered the broken pieces tenderly, found the leaves, tried to put them on to the thin, smashed branches, tried to put the pathetic little twigs back on to the fractured trunk of the tree. But they didn't stay, of course. She willed them to weld themselves together again, but they didn't. They stayed there while her shaking fingers held them, and then they just fell away, and only the stump remained.

When Emmie saw that no possible miracle could bring the apricot tree back to life, she cried. She just went on kneeling there, with her shoulders slumped and her hands covering her face, and cried. Quietly and without hope.

And then she felt herself being lifted up. Ridd stood her gently on her feet, turned her towards him, pulled her into his arms and cradled her head against his khaki shirt.

'Don't, Emily,' he pleaded, and his voice was so deep and husky that she hardly recognised it. 'I can stand anything—or I thought I could—but not that. Not that you should cry. Please, Emmie, you mustn't cry like that.' And then, because she couldn't seem to stop the sorrow that was welling up inside her, and the tears that were running through her fingers, his hold somehow tightened, and his own fingers buried her face even deeper against his broad khaki chest. 'Don't, Emmie. For God's sake, darling, hush! I understand, of course I do! I understand more than you think, much more than you suspect, my little, wilful, independent, pioneering sweetheart. But you mustn't weep like this. You mustn't cry, Emmie. You don't belong here, really, don't you see? You don't belong. It's not the place for you, this place, a lonely store at the back of nowhere. You're young and lovely and fresh and sweet. Too young and lovely and sweet to spend the rest of your life out here all alone, like your little apricot tree might have done. You don't belong here alone, my darling. You belong with me.'

'Ridd—what are you saying?'

She raised a tear-stained face and took in his own almost savagely-controlled features, shook her head disbelievingly, light-headed at the welter of confusion his words had brought to her already distraught mind.

'You—you can't know what you're saying,' she protested slowly, with a conviction that was meant as much to bring herself back to reality as anything else.

'Of course I know what I'm saying'—Ridd's chuckle was brief, without mirth—'only I hadn't meant to say it *yet*. Not yet, nor maybe possibly for quite a while after this, either. I meant to give you time, to forget about that other brutal business, the things I said and did, to forgive me if you could, so that we could start all over again, with a clean slate rubbed free of past mistakes and stupid misunderstandings. Take it slowly, Ridd, I said to myself. Give her time to forget, time to adjust. Be patient and careful, and maybe if you do all that, and take your time about it, maybe you'll be lucky enough to make her feel—*some* day—the same way as you feel about her.'

'Oh, *Ridd*!' Emmie's eyes were brimming again. Not just with tears, but with a love for him that seemed to catch her up on a great, wonderful tide that was so overwhelming, so exquisite, that it was also curiously unbearable.

'How could I know?' she whispered, and he tipped her

chin up so that he could gaze steadily and intently, right into her pale, oval, upturned face, and read the truth there for himself.

'How could I *know*?' she repeated, gazing back like a sleeper stepping right into a lovely dream. She hid her face against him. Now, if ever, was the time to start wiping clean that slate. Most of the misunderstandings were of her own making, anyway!

'Ridd, I have to tell you something,' she confessed in strangled but determined tones. 'I—I've been terribly deceitful. I—there wasn't any affair, Ridd. I deceived you terribly. There wasn't even any—any rebound. That wasn't why I came. And I—I d-don't know much about kissing, either.'

She felt a ripple of laughter run right through him. Felt it against the side of her cheek.

'Is that so, now?' He sounded severe, but when his fingers found her chin again and forced her to look at him, she was surprised to see that the grey eyes weren't angry at all. They too were brimming with laughter. 'What a little deceiver you are, to be sure! But I knew it already, what you've just told me, Emmie.'

'Knew it? How?' She was bewildered. One could never tell with Ridd. How would one ever be able to fathom what he knew, and what he didn't know?

'I knew it, right in the middle of kissing you that time. I was devilish angry, as you know—a combination of jealousy and frustration, I should think. I meant to punish you for what you were doing to me, and for your callousness in leading Kevin on when you'd admitted it meant nothing. And then, right in the middle of kissing you, it suddenly got through to me that somehow I'd plunged you in at the deep end before you'd even swum the shallows.'

'How could you possibly——'

'I was shaken. Pretty thoroughly shaken. I could see what I'd done to you too, and I—thought—oh, hell!——' Ridd came to a husky halt, ran his fingers through his hair despairingly, finally forced himself to continue. 'I got to thinking about how nothing seemed to add up, where you were concerned. I thought it out from every angle, and it didn't square somehow. And then when I found you so desperately sick the day I came over with the telephone engineer, I knew you meant everything in the world to me, Emmie, that I couldn't live without you, that I had to have you, that I couldn't go on with this pretence much longer.'

He stopped again.

'Ridd, I knew it when you danced with me. I just felt your arms around me, and I wanted it to mean something. I wanted it to mean *everything*, and I knew it couldn't, and my safe, carefully thought-out future seemed to mean nothing any more. It just seemed to collapse in smithereens at my feet. I realised I loved you then, but I couldn't afford to even let myself recognise the fact, it was all so impossible. I stumbled around in such a daze, a panic almost, knowing that from that moment on everything I did would be *second*-best to the thing I wanted most in life—the children, the store—yes, even the children—it didn't seem to mean the same any more, but I made myself go on. You have to go on, you know. I kept saying, if the little apricot tree is there, keeping pace with me, sharing my struggle, I can do it. And then—then——'

His arms tightened.

'That day I came over and found you, I made up my mind to do something about it, although I hadn't the least idea of how I was going to win you over after that despicable kiss I'd put you through. You really shook me when you said things might have been different if I hadn't given you that kiss, I can tell you!'

'*I* said *that*?'

'You did.' He sounded grim.

'I don't remember——'

'I spoke to Kevin after that. I was a bit desperate, I reckon, and there was plenty of time for the two of us to talk, hanging around waiting for you to get better.' A pause. 'He told me what you'd done for him, how you'd helped so much with himself and Sue.' Another pause. 'I knew, then, that there was more to it than met the eye, things I'd need to know. That's why I left for Sydney straight away.'

'For Sydney?' Her eyes were wide.

'I took a long shot, Emmie.' He was holding her gaze now, compelling her to attend to what he had to say. 'I went straight to Mark. No, stay still, we have to have this out.' His tone, his expression, were the old, masterful, forbidding ones, as he held her right where she was, when she would have struggled to escape those encircling arms.

'To—Mark? H-how did you know anything about Mark?' she queried feebly, sensing his change of mood.

'I didn't, not for sure. As I said, I played a hunch, that's all.' He laughed a little grimly. 'I couldn't afford not to play hunches, at that stage, however unlikely they may have seemed. *This* one paid off.'

'It did?'

'It did. Emmie, don't look like that. There's no need, darling. I'm on *your* side where that selfish, brilliant, delightful, *overbearing* family of yours is concerned. You'll never have to tackle them alone again so long as you live. *I'll* handle them from now on. I told them just what I thought of them, some of it good, some of it bad'—he grinned reminiscently—'and I reckon we understand each other pretty well now. I told them they'd crushed the tender flower, the fragile, beautiful little selfless one, that they'd exploited her shamefully (through sheer damn thoughtlessness, probably), and that they'd been so taken up with their own glamorous, ambitious, self-interested lives that they hadn't given a thought to what they were doing to her in the process. They missed you like hell, it may interest you to know, once they hadn't got you there to wait on them hand and foot, after you'd gone!' His lip curled lopsidedly. 'I gave them their come-uppance. I told them that *if* they want to come to our wedding, *if* they want to count *me* in on the family scene, they'd better start cultivating a little more consideration for people, a little sensitivity, and not ride roughshod over the gentler member of their family any more.'

'Oh, *Ridd*, you didn't!' she exclaimed faintly. 'You couldn't have said that—that bit about a—a *wedding*. Not *then*, Ridd. I mean, you—we—you hadn't——'

'I hadn't,' he admitted ruefully, with a twinkle, 'but I'm doing it now, Emmie, my sweet and only love. I'm asking you to be my wife.' He became suddenly grave, tender. 'Marry me, Emmie, please, will you, darling? I can't go on like this much longer.'

'I—Ridd, are you really sure? I mean, I—well, I'm so—ordinary.'

He gathered her into his arms.

'So sweet,' he murmured into her hair. 'So small and tender and sweet and appealing. Hasn't anyone ever told you what a perfect little oval face you have, what enormous misty eyes under all those sweeping lashes, such soft, silky hair that's as full of sunshine as a sunbeam itself?'

She shook her head, demurely.

'No one. Not ever.'

'Well, *I'm* telling you, Emmie. I've wanted to tell you for so long, almost since the very beginning——'

'Ridd.' She'd been thinking, or trying to. It was difficult to be sensible at a time like this. 'What about the children, if we——'

'*When* we,' he corrected her with a touch of his old arrogance. 'When we're married, and they reach secondary stage, they'll board in Berroola and come home at weekends. They can come to Koolonga now. There's enough room in that rambling homestead for a regiment of children, our own included.'

Her cheeks became a little pink.

'I must say I've loved looking after them,' she said swiftly, to cover that tell-tale blush. 'And the Homes have been more than adequate in their assistance. I managed much better than I thought I possibly could. I worried a lot about it, just at first, you know, but with those monthly cheques coming in, and the revenue from the store too, it was easy. I must thank the Matron for her generosity when we tell them about the change of plan.'

Ridd scratched his ear. He looked uncomfortable. Not like Riddley Fenton at all. Not like the Master-of-the-Situation.

'I—er—don't think I'd mention it, actually, if I were you, Emily.'

'Why not? After all, it was decent of them, those regular bank drafts, don't you think, so why not tell them so?'

'Yes—well——' his own colour deepened beneath the heavy tan—'you know what I'm trying to say. Official dispensations, Emmie, Government departments, local authorities, they—er—well, it's not usual to thank them. Much better not. Much better just to say nothing.'

'Why are you mumbling like that, Ridd?'

'Mumbling? Who's mumbling? I'm simply saying that it's more diplomatic not to mention the matter to the Matron at all,' he replied. But it had a lame sound. Suspiciously lame!

'Do you know what I think, Ridd?'

'What, Emmie?'

'I don't think that's what happened at all,' stated Emmie with quiet certainty. 'I don't think those monthly drafts even *came* from the matron, from the authorities, Ridd. I think they came from you. I'm right, aren't I?' The guilt of it was written all over his face. 'Why, Ridd? Why?'

'Can't you guess?' There was such an enveloping tenderness in his eyes that she couldn't prevent herself from putting up a hand to touch his cheek in an impulsive gesture of gratitude, respect, love that was overwhelming.

Ridd put his own hand over hers. She could feel the warmth of his fingers curling over her own fingers, keeping them there against his weathered brown cheek.

'I wanted you to stay, even then,' he confessed gently, and the controlled passion in him deepened his voice to a whisper. 'I had to keep you here somehow, and I knew even then that it was the kids that might hold you. If you were managing financially with them, I knew you'd stay.' A pause. 'I never meant you to know,' he confessed gruffly.

'Ridd, I love you so much I feel I'll die of it.'

She stood on tiptoe, and touched her lips to his chin. That was as far as she could reach, unless he bent his head.

'Darling'—the word wasn't very distinct, but she caught it—'there are kisses, and kisses, Emmie. I've been wanting to tell you that, my precious one, ever since that—other time.'

'Are there?'

'Yes, there are.'

'Show me, Ridd.'

And he did. His kiss was everything that that other one hadn't been, somehow. A kiss of discovery, that began somewhere near her ear, and travelled as light as a butterfly's breath, over her cheek, across to the corner of her mouth. It was a slow kiss, yet compelling. Magnetic, yet very, very tender.

Ridd lifted his head.

'That's the theme,' he told her huskily, and his eyes were crinkling already into a teasing caress that melted her bones, and his lips were curving gently into one of those endearing, lopsided smiles that made her heart turn right over and skip a couple of beats. 'The variations come later,' he added, as he took her hand and led her back to the house.

'We'll just lock up again, Emily, and then I'm taking you home.'

L

M　　　　　　　　　　　　　　　　　　　　　　　　　　GHL 972

FREE!
Harlequin Romance Catalogue

Here is a wonderful opportunity to read many of the Harlequin Romances you may have missed.

The HARLEQUIN ROMANCE CATALOGUE lists hundreds of titles which possibly are no longer available at your local bookseller. To receive your copy, just fill out the coupon below, mail it to us, and we'll rush your catalogue to you!

Following this page you'll find a sampling of a few of the Harlequin Romances listed in the catalogue. Should you wish to order any of these immediately, kindly check the titles desired and mail with coupon.

F

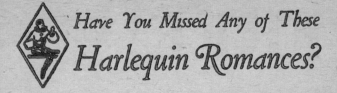

Have You Missed Any of These Harlequin Romances?

- ☐ 1256 THE PINK JACARANDA
  Juliet Shore
- ☐ 1261 WITH ALL MY HEART
  Nan Asquith
- ☐ 1264 SECRET STAR
  Marguerite Lees
- ☐ 1270 THOUGH WORLDS APART
  Mary Burchell
- ☐ 1272 DEVON INTERLUDE
  Kay Thorpe
- ☐ 1274 MAN FROM THE SEA
  Pamela Kent
- ☐ 1275 SHAKE OUT THE STARS
  Janice Gray
- ☐ 1280 THE FLIGHT OF THE SWAN
  Eleanor Farnes
- ☐ 1282 THE SHINING STAR
  Hilary Wilde
- ☐ 1283 ROSALIND COMES HOME
  Essie Summers
- ☐ 1284 ONLY MY HEART TO GIVE
  Nan Asquith
- ☐ 1285 OUT OF A DREAM
  Jean Curtis
- ☐ 1286 BE MORE THAN DREAMS
  Elizabeth Hoy
- ☐ 1287 THE WALLED GARDEN
  Margaret Malcolm
- ☐ 1288 THE LAST OF THE KINTYRES
  Catherine Airlie
- ☐ 1290 A SUMMER TO LOVE
  Roumelia Lane
- ☐ 1291 MASTER OF GLENKEITH
  Jean S. Macleod
- ☐ 1293 I KNOW MY LOVE
  Sara Seale
- ☐ 1294 THE BREADTH OF HEAVEN
  Rosemary Pollock
- ☐ 1296 THE WIND AND THE SPRAY
  Joyce Dingwell
- ☐ 1299 THE LISTENING PALMS
  Juliet Shore
- ☐ 1301 HOTEL BY THE LOCH
  Iris Danbury
- ☐ 1303 STILL WATERS
  Marguerite Lees
- ☐ 1304 SHARLIE FOR SHORT
  Dorothy Rivers
- ☐ 1306 A HANDFUL OF SILVER
  Isobel Chace

- ☐ 1376 SHADOWS FROM THE SEA
  Jane Donnelly
- ☐ 1380 RELUCTANT MASQUERADE
  Henrietta Reid
- ☐ 1381 MUSIC ON THE WIND
  Dorothy Slide
- ☐ 1382 TO JOURNEY TOGETHER
  Mary Burchell
- ☐ 1383 A WIFE FOR ANDREW
  Lucy Gillen
- ☐ 1388 UNWARY HEART
  Anne Hampson
- ☐ 1389 MAN OF FOREST
  Hilda Pressley
- ☐ 1390 SUGAR IN THE MORNING
  Isobel Chace
- ☐ 1391 MY VALIANT FLEDGLING
  Margaret Malcolm
- ☐ 1392 THAT YOUNG PERSON
  Sara Seale
- ☐ 1395 TERMINUS TEHRAN
  Roumelia Lane
- ☐ 1396 BRIGHT WILDERNESS
  Gwen Westwood
- ☐ 1397 IF LOVE WERE WISE
  Elizabeth Hoy
- ☐ 1399 BLUE JASMINE
  Violet Winspear
- ☐ 1416 SUMMER IN DECEMBER
  Essie Summers
- ☐ 1421 PARISIAN ADVENTURE
  Elizabeth Ashton
- ☐ 1422 THE SOPHISTICATED URCHIN
  Rosalie Heneghan
- ☐ 1423 SULLIVAN'S REEF
  Anne Weale
- ☐ 1424 THE VENGEFUL HEART
  Roberta Leigh
- ☐ 1553 DOCTOR TOBY
  Lucy Gillen
- ☐ 1554 THE KEYS OF THE CASTLE
  Barbara Rowan
- ☐ 1555 RAINTREE VALLEY
  Violet Winspear
- ☐ 1556 NO ENEMY
  Hilda Nickson
- ☐ 1557 ALONG THE RIBBONWOOD
  TRACK   Mary Moore
- ☐ 1558 LEGEND OF ROSCANO
  Iris Danbury

All books listed are 50c.   Please use the handy order coupon.
D